Mathematics

Author
Clive Morris

Series editor
Alan Brewerton

A level

Revision Notes

Letts
EDUCATIONAL

Every effort has been made to trace copyright holders and to obtain their permission for the use of copyright material. The authors and publishers will gladly receive information enabling them to rectify any error or omission in subsequent editions.

First published 1998

Letts Educational, Schools and Colleges Division, 9–15 Aldine Street, London W12 8AW
Tel. 0181 740 2270
Fax 0181 740 2280

Text © Clive Morris 1998

Editorial, design and production by Hart McLeod, Cambridge

British Library Cataloguing-in-Publication Data

A CIP record for this book is available from the British Library

ISBN 1 84085 092 2

Printed and bound in Great Britain

Letts Educational is the trading name of BPP (Letts Educational) Ltd

Contents

Introduction   **4**

1   Algebraic skills   **7**

2   Functions   **16**

3   Equations and inequalities   **25**

4   Indices and logarithms   **34**

5   Sequences and series   **40**

6   Coordinate geometry   **47**

7   Trigonometry   **53**

8   Calculus 1: differentiation   **64**

9   Calculus 2: integration   **73**

10   Numerical methods   **85**

11   Vectors   **88**

12   Probability   **92**

13   Statistics   **97**

Answers   **101**

Index   **120**

Introduction

Some useful tips for revising A Level Mathematics

This book is designed to give you the main notes needed to act as a focus to your revision. It will not be a substitute for making full use of the notes that you have taken during your course, or the notes you have taken from textbooks.

It is vital that you get yourself organised for revision. You need to focus your revision on:

- Understanding the main points of each topic.

- Learning formulae and other information.

- Managing the resources you will have.

1. Understanding the main points of each topic.

You will find it helpful to:

- Read through this book and your course notes and make sure that you understand all that is in them. Add to them where this will help your understanding later in the revision period.

- Refer to relevant sections in textbook(s) in order to get a different perspective on what you have learnt or to clear up areas that you still don't understand. Don't forget to talk to your teachers and friends to help you overcome difficulties too.

- Make a note of where these sections are for future reference.

2. Learning formulae and other information.

There is really no substitute for learning. Mathematics is a language just like German or French. No-one would try and suggest that you don't have to learn things in these – the same is true in Mathematics. It is important that you spend time committing relevant formulae and important techniques to memory.

While you will have a formulae book in the exam, you will save time and be able to solve problems more easily if you have learnt all the necessary formulae.

3. Managing the resources you will have.

It is important that you are aware which formulae are and aren't in your formulae booklet and that you can find your way around it quickly and efficiently in the examinations. You do not want to waste time chasing around looking for things during the examination only to find they are not in there.

Equally it is important that you master fully how to use your calculator. You are not allowed to have the instruction manual for that in the examinations! Time spent now looking up how to use it for particular calculations, e.g. in statistics, and practising using it properly will pay dividends in the examination.

Some final thoughts

While revising and practising questions in this book and from other past papers **get into good habits now**.

- Read each question **carefully**.

- Lay out your work **neatly** and **logically** with clear handwriting, show your working and explain what you are doing when appropriate.

- Try and avoid the common pitfalls in each topic area – let others make those sorts of mistakes but not you.

- Don't round your answer until the end of a question – it can cause rounding errors and lose you marks.

- Make sure you give the answers to questions in the form asked for in the question, e.g. in terms of natural logarithms, in surd form etc.

- Learn what the examiners are looking for. Get hold of old mark schemes and find out how marks are allocated. Go to revision conferences run by Principal and Chief Examiners if you can.

- Your goal is to gain the most marks possible in the time available.

Algebraic skills

Algebraic statements

Make sure you understand the difference between the following types of algebraic statements.

| **Expressions** | e.g. | (i) | $x^2 + 3$ | You are often asked to **simplify** expressions. |
| | | (ii) | $\sin 3\theta$ | |

| **Equations** | e.g. | (i) | $x^2 + 2x - 7 = 0$ | These are true for a limited number of values of x. You are often asked to **solve** equations. |
| | | (ii) | $2 \sin \left(x + \dfrac{\pi}{6}\right) = 0$ | |

| **Inequalities** | e.g. | (i) | $x^2 + 2x - 9 < 0$ | These are true for all values of x in a certain range. |
| | | (ii) | $e^{2x} \geq 1$ | |

| **Identities** | e.g. | (i) | $\sin^2 x + \cos^2 x \equiv 1$ | These are true for all values of x. |
| | | (ii) | $(x + 2)^2 \equiv x^2 + 4x + 4$ | |

| **Formulae** | e.g. | (i) | $F = \dfrac{9}{5}C + 32$ | These general statements link a number of variables and enable you to calculate the value of one of the variables when you know the values of the others. |
| | | (ii) | $x = \dfrac{-b \pm \sqrt{b^2 - 4ac}}{2a}$ | |

Algebraic techniques

Expanding brackets

Examples

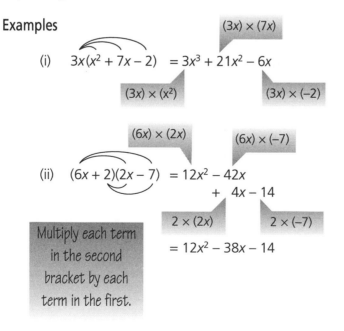

(i) $3x(x^2 + 7x - 2) = 3x^3 + 21x^2 - 6x$

$(3x) \times (7x)$

$(3x) \times (x^2)$ $(3x) \times (-2)$

(ii) $(6x + 2)(2x - 7) = 12x^2 - 42x$
$+ \; 4x - 14$

$(6x) \times (2x)$ $(6x) \times (-7)$

$2 \times (2x)$ $2 \times (-7)$

$= 12x^2 - 38x - 14$

Note this neat way of laying out the expansion to help avoid making errors when simplifying.

Multiply each term in the second bracket by each term in the first.

Putting over a common denominator

Examples

(i) $\dfrac{6}{2x-1} - \dfrac{3}{x^2-1} = \dfrac{6(x^2-1)}{(2x-1)(x^2-1)} - \dfrac{3(2x-1)}{(2x-1)(x^2-1)}$

$= \dfrac{6x^2-6-6x+3}{(2x-1)(x^2-1)}$

> Watch the sign here.

$= \dfrac{6x^2-6x-3}{(2x-1)(x^2-1)}$

$= \dfrac{3\,(2x^2-2x-1)}{(2x-1)(x^2-1)}$

> Make sure you factorise fully.

(ii) $\dfrac{6}{x-1} + \dfrac{7}{x^2-1} = \dfrac{6(x+1)+7}{x^2-1}$

$= \dfrac{6x+6+7}{x^2-1}$

$= \dfrac{6x+13}{x^2-1}$

> (x^2-1) is the common denominator here because $(x^2-1) = (x-1)(x+1)$.

Factorising

There are three types of factorising.

1 Highest common factor

> $(2x) \times (2y) = 4xy$

$$6x^2 + 4xy = 2x\,(3x + 2y)$$

> $2x$ is the highest common factor of $6x^2$ and $4xy$.

> $(2x) \times (3x) = 6x^2$

2 Two pairs of factors

$$3x^2 + 12x + 2xy + 8y = 3x\,(x+4) + 2y\,(x+4)$$
$$= (x+4)(3x+2y)$$

> If it doesn't work straight away try choosing the pairs differently.

> $(x+4)$ is now a common factor.

> Extract the highest common factor for each of the two pairs.

3 Quadratics

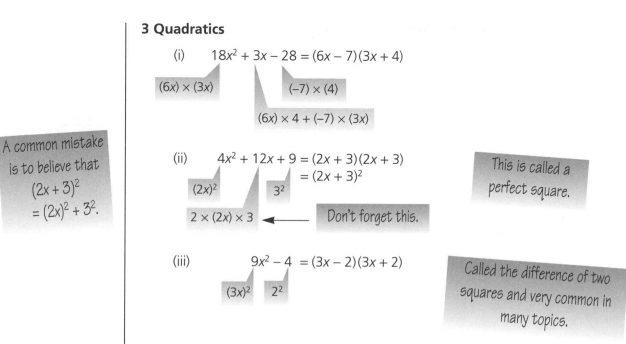

(i) $\quad 18x^2 + 3x - 28 = (6x - 7)(3x + 4)$

$(6x) \times (3x)$ $\qquad (-7) \times (4)$

$(6x) \times 4 + (-7) \times (3x)$

A common mistake is to believe that
$(2x + 3)^2$
$= (2x)^2 + 3^2.$

(ii) $\quad 4x^2 + 12x + 9 = (2x + 3)(2x + 3)$
$\qquad\qquad\qquad\qquad = (2x + 3)^2$

$(2x)^2$ $\qquad 3^2$

$2 \times (2x) \times 3 \longleftarrow$ Don't forget this.

This is called a perfect square.

(iii) $\qquad 9x^2 - 4 = (3x - 2)(3x + 2)$

$(3x)^2$ $\quad 2^2$

Called the difference of two squares and very common in many topics.

Rearranging formulae

A series of logical steps in which the same thing is done to both sides of a formula to change the subject.

Examples

(i) To make l the subject of $T = 2\pi\sqrt{\dfrac{l}{g}}$.

$2\pi\sqrt{\dfrac{l}{g}} = T$ $\qquad$ Write the formula with the new subject on the left.

$(2\pi)^2 \dfrac{l}{g} = T^2$ $\qquad$ Square each term on both sides.

$4\pi^2 l = T^2 g$ $\qquad$ Multiply both sides by g.

$l = \dfrac{T^2 g}{4\pi^2}$ $\qquad$ Divide both sides by $4\pi^2$.

(ii) To make x the subject of $y = \dfrac{2x + 3}{x - 1}$.

$(x - 1)y = 2x + 3$ $\qquad$ Multiply both sides by $(x - 1)$ to get rid of the fraction.

$xy - y = 2x + 3$ $\qquad$ Expand the brackets.

$xy - 2x = y + 3$ $\qquad$ Collect all terms involving the new subject on the left.

$x(y - 2) = y + 3$ $\qquad$ Factorise.

$x = \dfrac{y + 3}{y - 2}$ $\qquad$ Divide both sides by $(y - 2)$ to leave x on its own.

Manipulating surds

Examples

(i) $$3\sqrt{2} + 7\sqrt{2} = 10\sqrt{2}$$

(ii) $$\sqrt{18} + \sqrt{162} = \sqrt{9 \times 2} + \sqrt{81 \times 2}$$
$$= \sqrt{9}\sqrt{2} + \sqrt{81}\sqrt{2}$$
$$= 3\sqrt{2} + 9\sqrt{2}$$
$$= 12\sqrt{2}$$

> Take out the factors which are square numbers, i.e. 9 and 81 here.

(iii) $$\left(5\sqrt{2} + 3\sqrt{3}\right)\left(2\sqrt{3} - \sqrt{2}\right) = 10\sqrt{2}\sqrt{3} - 5\left(\sqrt{2}\right)^2 + 6\left(\sqrt{3}\right)^2 - 3\sqrt{3}\sqrt{2}$$
$$= 10\sqrt{2}\sqrt{3} - (5 \times 2) + (6 \times 3) - 3\sqrt{3}\sqrt{2}$$
$$= 7\sqrt{2}\sqrt{3} + 8$$
$$= 7\sqrt{6} + 8$$

(iv) $$\frac{12}{\sqrt{3}} = \frac{12}{\sqrt{3}} \times \frac{\sqrt{3}}{\sqrt{3}}$$
$$= \frac{12\sqrt{3}}{3}$$
$$= 4\sqrt{3}$$

(v) $$\frac{3 + 2\sqrt{2}}{\sqrt{3} - \sqrt{2}} = \frac{\left(3 + 2\sqrt{2}\right)}{\sqrt{3} - \sqrt{2}} \times \frac{\left(\sqrt{3} + \sqrt{2}\right)}{\left(\sqrt{3} + \sqrt{2}\right)}$$
$$= \frac{3\sqrt{3} + 3\sqrt{2} + 2\sqrt{2}\sqrt{3} + 2\left(\sqrt{2}\right)^2}{\left(\sqrt{3}\right)^2 + \sqrt{3}\sqrt{2} - \sqrt{3}\sqrt{2} - \left(\sqrt{2}\right)^2}$$
$$= \frac{3\sqrt{3} + 3\sqrt{2} + 2\sqrt{6} + 4}{3 - 2}$$
$$= 3\sqrt{3} + 3\sqrt{2} + 2\sqrt{6} + 4$$

> Multiply numerator and denominator by the term that will make the denominator the difference of two squares.

Polynomials

- A polynomial is of the form

  $$a_0 + a_1x + a_2x^2 + a_3x^3 + \ldots + a_nx^n, \ n \in \mathbb{Z}_+$$

  where $a_0, a_1, a_2, \ldots, a_n$ are constants or coefficients. The **degree** of this polynomial is the largest power of x. The degree of $2 + 3x + x^7$ would therefore be 7.

- Polynomials can be added, subtracted, multiplied or divided. (For division see rational functions on page 11.)

Examples

(i) $(3 + 2x + 2x^2 - 3x^3) + (7 - 5x + 2x^2 - x^3)$
$= 3 + 7 + 2x - 5x + 2x^2 + 2x^2 - 3x^3 - x^3$
$= 10 - 3x + 4x^2 - 4x^3$

(ii) $(6 + 2x - 4x^3) - (4 - 4x + 7x^2)$
$= 6 - 4 + 2x - (-4x) - 4x^3 - 7x^2$
$= 2 + 6x - 7x^2 - 4x^3$

(iii)　$(3 + 4x + 2x^3) \times (1 - x - x^3)$

$= 3(1 - x - x^3) + 4x\,(1 - x - x^3) + 2x^3\,(1 - x - x^3)$

$= 3 - 3x \qquad\quad - 3x^3$

$\qquad\ 4x - 4x^2 \qquad\quad - 4x^4$

$\qquad\qquad\qquad 2x^3 - 2x^4 - 2x^6$

$= 3 +\ x - 4x^2\ - x^3 - 6x^4 - 2x^6$

Rational functions

- A rational function is of the form $\dfrac{p(x)}{q(x)}$, where $p(x)$ and $q(x)$ are both polynomials.

- If the degree of the numerator (the top) is greater than or equal to the degree of the denominator (the bottom) the rational function is said to be improper (otherwise it is called proper) and long division can be used to simplify it.

In this case $\dfrac{p(x)}{q(x)} = r(x) + \dfrac{u(x)}{q(x)}$,

where $r(x)$ and $u(x)$ are polynomials and the degree of $u(x)$ is less than the degree of $q(x)$. $u(x)$ is said to be the remainder when $p(x)$ is divided by $q(x)$.

Example

$$\frac{8x^4 + 4x^3 + 2x - 3}{x^2 + 1} = 8x^2 + 4x - 8 + \frac{-2x + 5}{x^2 + 1}$$

since

x^2 goes into $8x^4$, $8x^2$ times.

x^2 goes into $4x^3$, $4x$ times.

x^2 goes into $-8x^2$, -8 times.

$$
\begin{array}{r}
8x^2 + 4x - 8 \\
x^2 + 1\,\overline{\smash{)}\,8x^4 + 4x^3 + 0x^2 + 2x - 3} \\
\end{array}
$$

$-(8x^4 \qquad + 8x^2)$ ← $(8x^2) \times (x^2 + 1)$

$\qquad 4x^3 - 8x^2 + 2x$

$\quad -(4x^3 \qquad + 4x)$ ← $(4x) \times (x^2 + 1)$

$\qquad\quad -8x^2 - 2x - 3$

$\qquad -(-8x^2 \qquad - 8)$ ← $(-8) \times (x^2 + 1)$

$\qquad\qquad\quad -2x + 5$

Remainder.

- Another technique which can sometimes be useful when dealing with rational functions is **algebraic juggling**.

Example

$$\frac{x^2 + 2x - 1}{x - 1} = \frac{x\,(x - 1) + 3x - 1}{x - 1}$$

$$= \frac{x\,(x - 1) + 3\,(x - 1) + 2}{x - 1}$$

$$= \frac{(x + 3)\,(x - 1) + 2}{x - 1}$$

$$= x + 3 + \frac{2}{x - 1}$$

Remainder theorem

- If a polynomial $f(x)$ is divided by $(x - a)$ then the remainder r is given by evaluating $f(a)$.

- We can write $f(x) = (x - a)\, g(x) + r$, where $g(x)$ is another polynomial.

Example

The remainder when dividing $f(x) = 2x^3 - 7x^2 + 3$ by $(x - 3)$ is
$f(3) = 2 \times 3^3 - 7 \times 3^2 + 3 = -6$.

The remainder when dividing $q(x) = x^2 + 7x + 1$ by $(x + 1)$ is
$q(-1) = (-1)^2 + 7 \times (-1) + 1 = -5$.

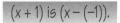

$(x + 1)$ is $(x - (-1))$.

Factor theorem

- This is a special case of the remainder theorem.

- If a polynomial $f(x)$ is such that $f(a) = 0$, then $(x - a)$ is a factor of $f(x)$.

Example

Find the factors of $f(x) = 2x^3 + 3x^2 - 3x - 2$.

$f(1) = 2 \times 1^3 + 3 \times 1^2 - 3 \times 1 - 2 = 0$ so $(x - 1)$ is a factor.

$f(-1) = 2 \times (-1)^3 + 3 \times (-1)^2 - 3 \times (-1) - 2 = 2$ so $(x + 1)$ is **not** a factor.

$f(2) = 2 \times 2^3 + 3 \times 2^2 - 3 \times 2 - 2 = 20$ so $(x - 2)$ is **not** a factor.

$f(-2) = 2 \times (-2)^3 + 3 \times (-2)^2 - 3 \times (-2) - 2 = 0$ so $(x + 2)$ is a factor.

This must be 1 because $-1 \times 2 \times 1 = -2$.

> It is easier to find the final factor in this way.

$f(x) = (x - 1)\,(x + 2)\,(2x + 1)$

This must be $2x$ because $x \times x \times 2x = 2x^3$.

Example

Factorise fully $f(x) = 2x^3 - 7x^2 - 3x + 18$.

$f(2) = 2 \times 2^3 - 7 \times 2^2 - 3 \times 2 + 18 = 16 - 28 - 6 + 18 = 0$
So $x - 2$ is a factor of $f(x)$.

Must be $2x^2$ to give $x \times 2x^2 = 2x^3$.

$f(x) = (x - 2)\,(2x^2 - 3x - 9)$

Must be -9 here to give $-2 \times -9 = 18$.

Must be $-3x$ here because $-2 \times 2x^2 = -4x^2$ and we need another $-3x^2$ to give $-7x^2$, i.e. $-3x \times x$.

$f(x) = (x - 2)\,(2x + 3)\,(x - 3)$

Partial fractions

There are a number of different methods for tackling partial fractions problems. The following method works for each of the three types of problem. Remember to use long division first if the rational function is improper.

Linear factors

$$\frac{ax + b}{(cx + d)(ex + f)} \equiv \frac{A}{cx + d} + \frac{B}{ex + f}$$

Example

$$\frac{5x - 4}{(2x - 1)(x - 2)} \equiv \frac{A}{2x - 1} + \frac{B}{x + 2}$$

$$5x - 4 \equiv A(x - 2) + B(2x - 1)$$

If $x = 2$ $6 = 3B$ Putting $x = 2$ makes the first term on the right hand side zero.

$$B = 3$$

If $x = \frac{1}{2}$ $\frac{-3}{2} = \frac{-3}{2}A$ Putting $2x = 1$ i.e. $x = \frac{1}{2}$ makes the second term on the right hand side zero.

$$A = 1$$

$$\frac{5x - 4}{(2x - 1)(x - 2)} \equiv \frac{1}{2x - 1} + \frac{3}{x - 2}$$

Linear and quadratic factors

$$\frac{ax^2 + bx + c}{(dx + e)(fx^2 + gx + h)} \equiv \frac{A}{dx + e} + \frac{Bx + C}{fx^2 + gx + h}, \text{ where } fx^2 + gx + h \text{ does not factorise.}$$

Example

$$\frac{2x^2 + x}{(x - 2)(x^2 + 1)} \equiv \frac{A}{x - 2} + \frac{Bx + C}{x^2 + 1}$$

$$2x^2 + x \equiv A(x^2 + 1) + (Bx + C)(x - 2)$$

If $x = 2$ $10 = 5A$ Putting $x = 2$ eliminates one term and leaves the term with only one constant.

$$A = 2$$

If $x = 0$ $0 = A - 2C$ Putting $x = 0$ eliminates one constant and we now know one other.

$$0 = 2 - 2C$$
$$C = 1$$

If $x = 1$ $3 = 2A + (B + C)(-1)$ Putting $x = 1$. We could have used any x value here other than those we have already used.
Choose simple values of x if possible.

$$3 = 2A - B - C$$
$$B = 2A - C - 3$$
$$B = 2 \times 2 - 1 - 3$$
$$B = 0$$

$$\frac{2x^2 + x}{(x - 2)(x^2 + 1)} \equiv \frac{2}{x - 2} + \frac{1}{x^2 + 1}$$

Be careful to get the signs right.

Repeated linear factors

$$\frac{ax^2 + bx + c}{(dx + e)(fx + g)^2} \equiv \frac{A}{dx + e} + \frac{B}{fx + g} + \frac{C}{(fx + g)^2}$$

Example

$$\frac{3x^2 - x - 1}{(x - 2)(x + 1)^2} \equiv \frac{A}{x - 2} + \frac{B}{x + 1} + \frac{C}{(x + 1)^2}$$

$$3x^2 - x - 1 \equiv A(x + 1)^2 + B(x + 1)(x - 2) + C(x - 2)$$

If $x = 2$ $9 = 9A$ Putting $x = 2$ eliminates all but one constant.

               $A = 1$

If $x = -1$ $3 = -3C$ Putting $x = -1$ eliminates all but one constant.

               $C = -1$

If $x = 0$ $-1 = A - 2B - 2C$ Putting $x = 0$. Any other x value will work but this

               $2B = A + 1 - 2C$ one makes the calculation a little easier.

               $2B = 1 + 1 + 2$

               $2B = 4$

               $B = 2$

$$\frac{3x^2 - x - 1}{(x - 2)(x + 1)^2} \equiv \frac{1}{x - 2} + \frac{2}{x + 1} - \frac{1}{(x + 1)^2}$$

Questions

1 Simplify each of the following expressions:

   (a) $\dfrac{x}{x-2} - \dfrac{x-2}{x}$

   (b) $(2x^2 - 3)(3x^2 + 2x - 7)$

   (c) $\dfrac{1}{x^2 - 1} + \dfrac{2x}{2x^2 + x - 3}$

   (d) $\dfrac{x^2 + 3x}{x^2 - 4} \div \dfrac{x^2 + 5x + 6}{2x^2 + 3x - 14}$

2 Factorise each of the following as fully as possible:

   (a) $3x^2 + 7x + 6xy + 14y$

   (b) $16x^2 - 24x + 9$

   (c) $8x^2y + 6xy^2 - 14x^3y^3$

   (d) $6x^2 - 13x - 33$

   (e) $9x^2 - 4y^2$

   (f) $x - 3\sqrt{x} - 4$

3 Rearrange each of the following to make x the subject:

   (a) $y^2 + 3 = \sqrt{\dfrac{x+2}{7}}$

   (b) $y = \dfrac{3x+7}{7-2x}$

4 Simplify each of the following:

   (a) $\sqrt{180} + \sqrt{20}$

   (b) $\dfrac{18}{\sqrt{2}}$

   (c) $\dfrac{6\sqrt{2} - 3\sqrt{3}}{5\sqrt{3} - 2\sqrt{2}}$

   (d) $\left(7\sqrt{2} + 4\sqrt{7}\right)\left(2\sqrt{7} - \sqrt{2}\right)$

5 Use long division to evaluate $(3x^4 + 2x^3 - 3x^2 + 1) \div (x - 2)$.

6 Find the remainder when:

   (a) $2x^3 + x - 7$ is divided by $x - 3$

   (b) $3x^4 - x^3 + 6$ is divided by $x + 4$

7 Factorise fully:

   (a) $2x^3 + 7x^2 - 7x - 12$

   (b) $3x^3 + 4x^2 - 17x - 6$

8 The remainder when $3x^3 - 6x^2 + ax - 1$ is divided by $(x + 1)$ is twice the remainder obtained when the same expression is divided by $(x - 3)$. Find the value of a.

9 Write each of the following in partial fractions:

   (a) $\dfrac{8-x}{(2x-1)(x+2)}$

   (b) $\dfrac{5x^2 + 12x + 10}{(x+1)(x^2 + x + 1)}$

   (c) $\dfrac{6x^2 - 7x + 3}{x(x-1)^2}$

   (d) $\dfrac{3x^3 + 4x^2 - 8x - 18}{(x+1)(x-2)}$

   (e) $\dfrac{x^2 + 3x - 13}{(x+2)(x-1)}$

Functions

Make sure you use
the form asked for
in the question.

- A **function** is a rule which assigns values to a set of numbers.

- There are two important types of notation.

$$f(x) = \sin x, \qquad 0 \leq x \leq \pi$$
$$f: x \rightarrow \sin x, \qquad 0 \leq x \leq \pi$$

- Notice that in each case the **domain** (the numbers put into the function) is stated as well as the rule defining the function. If no domain is stated it may be assumed to be all the real numbers.

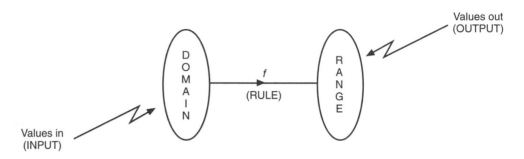

- In the example above the range of f is $0 \leq f(x) \leq 1$.

- The image of $\frac{\pi}{4}$ is said to be $\frac{1}{\sqrt{2}}$ because $\sin \frac{\pi}{4} = \frac{1}{\sqrt{2}}$

- A function can be **many-to-one** or **one-to-one** but never one-to-many as shown in the diagrams below.

One-to-one
functions are the
only ones that have
inverses.

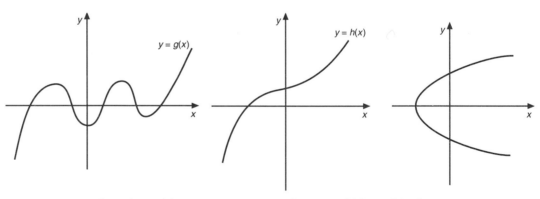

A many-to-one function $g(x)$. A one-to-one function $h(x)$. This does not represent
If $x_1 \neq x_2$, $f(x_1) \neq f(x_2)$. a function.

Types of function

There are three special types of function.

Type of function	Condition	Properties of the graph
Odd	$f(-x) = -f(x)$	Rotation symmetry of order 2 about the origin.
Even	$f(-x) = f(x)$	Reflection symmetry in the y-axis.
Periodic	$f(x) = f(x + p)$	Repeats itself every p units travelled along the x-axis.

Examples

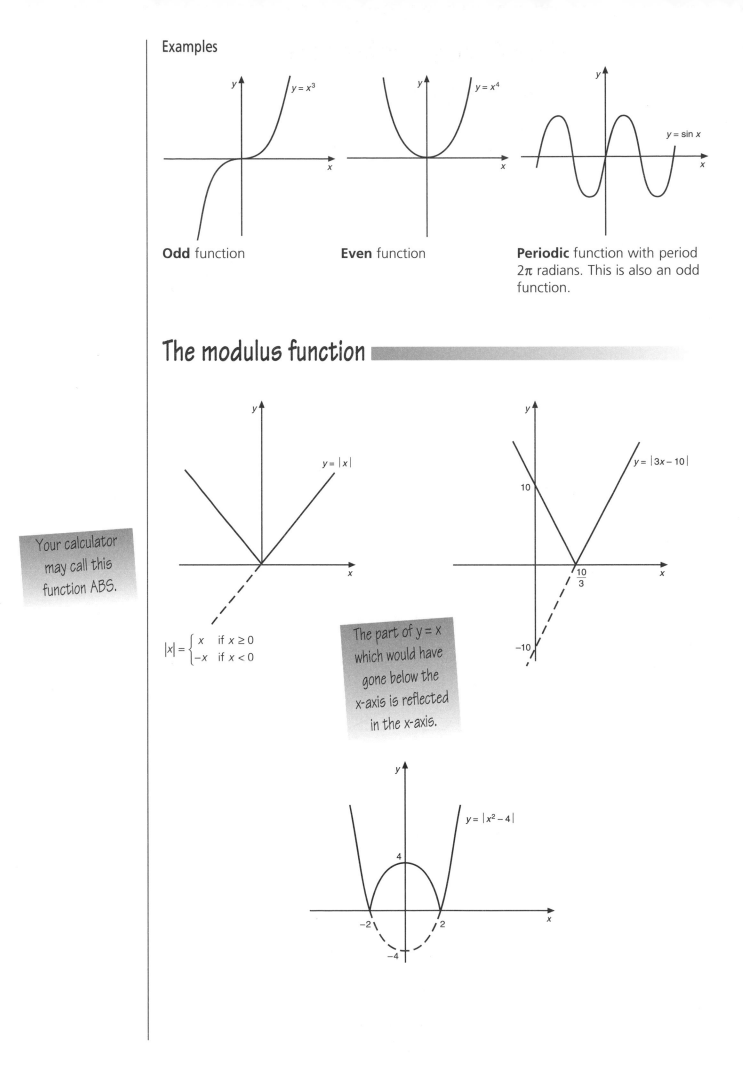

Odd function

Even function

Periodic function with period 2π radians. This is also an odd function.

The modulus function

Your calculator may call this function ABS.

$y = |x|$

$$|x| = \begin{cases} x & \text{if } x \geq 0 \\ -x & \text{if } x < 0 \end{cases}$$

The part of $y = x$ which would have gone below the x-axis is reflected in the x-axis.

$y = |3x - 10|$

$y = |x^2 - 4|$

Transformation of functions

Types of transformations

Example

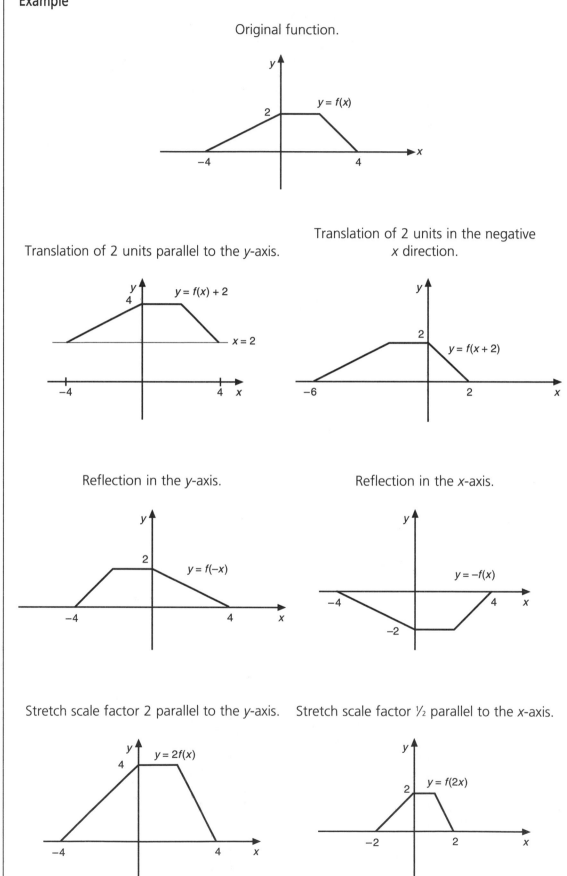

Original function.

Translation of 2 units parallel to the *y*-axis.

Translation of 2 units in the negative *x* direction.

Reflection in the *y*-axis.

Reflection in the *x*-axis.

Stretch scale factor 2 parallel to the *y*-axis.

Stretch scale factor ½ parallel to the *x*-axis.

These transformations are often confused, particularly the last two.

Combinations of transformations can be built up from their components.

Example

To find the graph of $y = -2f(3x) + 1$ if $f(x)$ has the graph:

$y = f(x)$

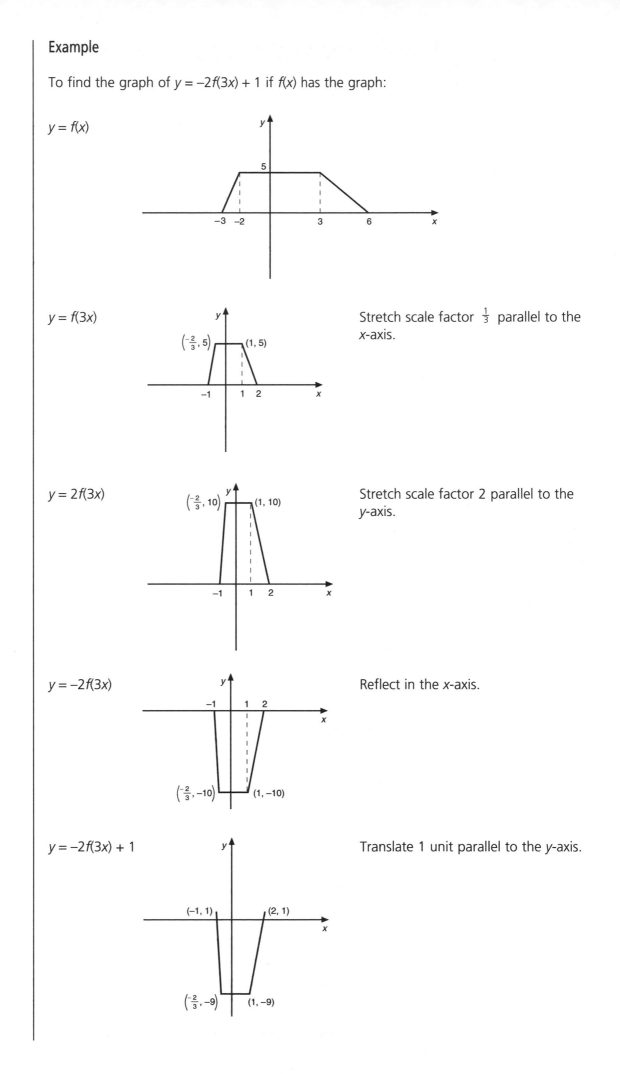

$y = f(3x)$

Stretch scale factor $\frac{1}{3}$ parallel to the x-axis.

$y = 2f(3x)$

Stretch scale factor 2 parallel to the y-axis.

$y = -2f(3x)$

Reflect in the x-axis.

$y = -2f(3x) + 1$

Translate 1 unit parallel to the y-axis.

Composite functions

- $fg(x)$ or $f(g(x))$ or $f_og(x)$ means do g to x first and then put the answer into f.

Example

If $g(x) = x^2$ and $f(x) = x + 2$

$\quad fg(x) = f(x^2) = x^2 + 2$

Note that $gf(x) = g(x + 2) = (x + 2)^2$

Further, if $h(x) = \dfrac{1}{x}$

$hfg(x) = hf(x^2) = h(x^2 + 2) = \dfrac{1}{x^2 + 2}$

Note that $h^2(x)$ means $hh(x)$,

i.e. $h^2(x) = \dfrac{1}{\left(\dfrac{1}{x}\right)} = x$

As we shall see later this means that h is the **inverse** of h, i.e. h is a **self-inversing function**.

Inverse functions

- A function f has an inverse if and only if f is a one-to-one function.
- In such cases if $f : c \to d$ then the inverse $f^{-1} : d \to c$.
- The range of f = the domain of f^{-1}
- The range of f^{-1} = the domain of f.

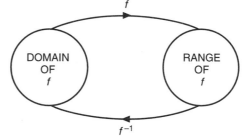

- If $uv(x) = x$ this means that $u = v^{-1}$ since u sends $v(x)$ back to x.

- f^{-1} means the inverse of f and **not** $\dfrac{1}{f(x)}$.

- The graph of the inverse function $y = f^{-1}(x)$ is the reflection of the graph of $y = f(x)$ in the line $y = x$ (mirror line).

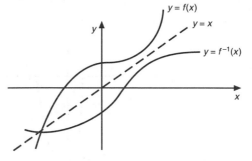

The inverse of a composite function $fg(x)$ is $g^{-1}f^{-1}(x)$, i.e. the inverses of each function applied in **the opposite order**.

Usually
$fg(x) \not\equiv gf(x)$.

Finding inverse functions

There are two main methods of finding the inverse of a given function.

Method 1

Example

$$f(x) = \frac{x}{x-2}, \quad x \geq 2$$

$$y = \frac{x}{x-2}$$ Put y equal to the function.

$$(x-2)y = x$$ Rearrange to get x in terms of y.
$$xy - 2y = x$$
$$xy - x = 2y$$
$$x(y-1) = 2y$$

$$x = \frac{2y}{y-1}$$

$$y = \frac{2x}{x-1}$$ Swap x and y throughout. This is the crucial stage.

$$f^{-1}(x) = \frac{2x}{x-1}$$ This is the inverse of f.

$$f^{-1}(x) = \frac{2x}{x-1}, \quad x \geq 1$$ To finish it off you need the domain of f^{-1}. Remember this is the range of f and can be obtained easily from a sketch graph as below.

> Make sure that you give your answer in the form asked for in the question.

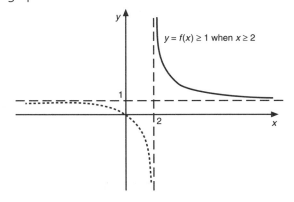

Method 2

This only works when x occurs once in the original expression for $f(x)$ or when $f(x)$ can be rearranged so that x only occurs once.

Example

In our previous example $f(x) = \dfrac{x}{x-2} = \dfrac{(x-2)+2}{x-2} = 1 + \dfrac{2}{x-2}$.

Analyse $f(x)$ using a flowchart approach

$$x \rightarrow \boxed{-2} \rightarrow \boxed{\tfrac{2}{}} \rightarrow \boxed{+1} \rightarrow f(x)$$

Do the opposite things in the opposite order.

$$f^{-1}(x) \leftarrow \boxed{+2} \leftarrow \boxed{\tfrac{2}{}} \leftarrow \boxed{-1} \leftarrow x$$
$$\underset{\frac{2}{x-1}+2}{} \quad \underset{\frac{2}{x-1}}{} \quad \underset{x-1}{}$$

So $f^{-1}(x) = \dfrac{2}{x-1} + 2 = \dfrac{2 + 2(x-1)}{x-1} = \dfrac{2x}{x-1}$ as before.

The rest of the working follows as before.

Solving equations involving $f^{-1}(x)$

Sometimes you will be asked to find the solutions of the equations $f^{-1}(x) = f(x)$ or something similar.

It is worth remembering that when $f^{-1}(x) = f(x)$, $f(x) = x = f^{-1}(x)$.
It is wise to select the easiest equation to solve as the following example shows.

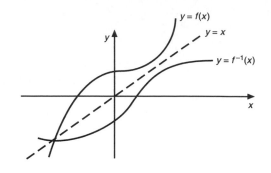

Example

The function $f(x)$ is defined by $f(x) = x^2 - 2$, $x \geq 0$.
Find the value of x for which $f(x) = f^{-1}(x)$.

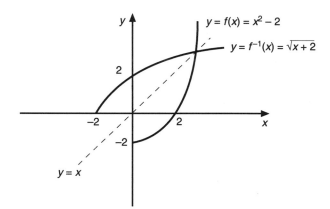

It can be shown that $f^{-1}(x) = \sqrt{x + 2}$, $x \geq -2$.

Solving $\quad x^2 - 2 = \sqrt{x + 2}$ is quite difficult.

Solving $\qquad\qquad f(x) = x$

i.e. $\quad x^2 - 2 = x$

$\qquad x^2 - x - 2 = 0 \qquad$ is much easier (and doesn't require us to find $f^{-1}(x)$ first!).

$\quad (x - 2)(x + 1) = 0$

$\qquad\qquad\qquad x = 2$ or -1

$\qquad\qquad\qquad x = 2$ since $x \geq 0$

Questions

1 Explain why if $y^2 = x$, $x > 0$ and $y = f(x)$, then $f(x)$ does not define a function.

2 Which of the following graphs illustrate one-to-one functions?

(a)

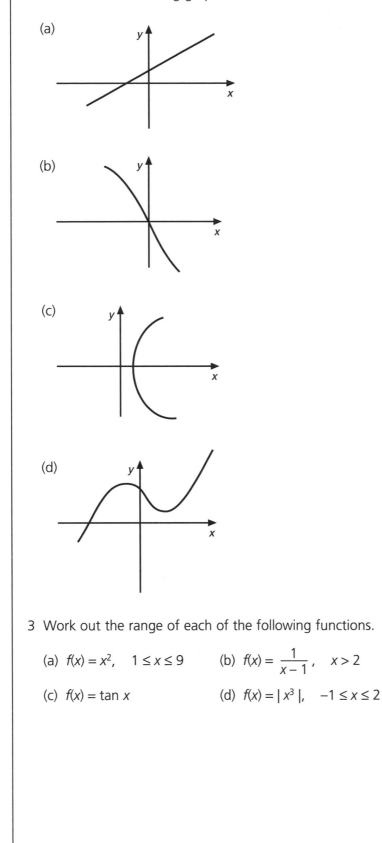

(b)

(c)

(d)

3 Work out the range of each of the following functions.

(a) $f(x) = x^2$, $1 \leq x \leq 9$

(b) $f(x) = \dfrac{1}{x-1}$, $x > 2$

(c) $f(x) = \tan x$

(d) $f(x) = |x^3|$, $-1 \leq x \leq 2$

4 Copy and complete each of the following graphs for $x < 0$ according to the condition stated.

(a)

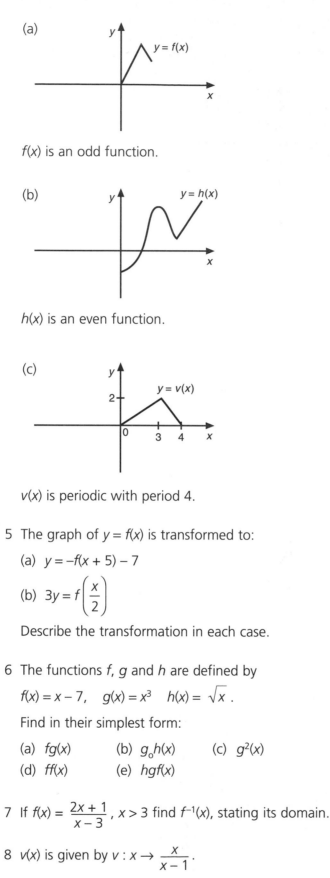

$f(x)$ is an odd function.

(b)

$h(x)$ is an even function.

(c)

$v(x)$ is periodic with period 4.

5 The graph of $y = f(x)$ is transformed to:

(a) $y = -f(x + 5) - 7$

(b) $3y = f\left(\dfrac{x}{2}\right)$

Describe the transformation in each case.

6 The functions f, g and h are defined by

$f(x) = x - 7, \quad g(x) = x^3 \quad h(x) = \sqrt{x}$.

Find in their simplest form:

(a) $fg(x)$ (b) $g_oh(x)$ (c) $g^2(x)$

(d) $ff(x)$ (e) $hgf(x)$

7 If $f(x) = \dfrac{2x + 1}{x - 3}$, $x > 3$ find $f^{-1}(x)$, stating its domain.

8 $v(x)$ is given by $v : x \rightarrow \dfrac{x}{x - 1}$.

(a) Find $v^2(x)$ in its simplest form.

(b) State what this shows about v and express v^{-1} in a similar form.

Equations and inequalities

Linear equations

There are a number of basic principles used when solving linear equations:

1 Expanding brackets.
2 Collecting together similar terms (simplifying).
3 Getting rid of fractions.
4 Doing the same things to both sides of the equation.

Examples

Watch the signs when you multiply out.

(i) Solve $\quad 4(x + 3) - 8(x - 2) = 5(x + 7) + 11$

$$4x + 12 - 8x + 16 = 5x + 35 + 11 \qquad \text{Expand the brackets.}$$
$$-4x + 28 = 5x + 46 \qquad \text{Collect similar terms.}$$
$$-9x + 28 = 46 \qquad \text{Subtract } 5x \text{ from each side.}$$
$$-9x = 18 \qquad \text{Subtract 28 from each side.}$$
$$x = -2 \qquad \text{Divide both sides by } -9.$$

Always go back and check that your answer works in the original equation.

Remember that fraction lines act as brackets, top and bottom.

(ii) Solve $\quad \dfrac{x + 2}{3} - \dfrac{3x + 1}{6} = \dfrac{x - 2}{12}$

$$\frac{12(x + 2)}{3} - \frac{12(3x + 1)}{6} = \frac{12(x - 2)}{12} \qquad \text{Multiply through by the lowest common denominator.}$$

$$4(x + 2) - 2(3x + 1) = x - 2 \qquad \text{Expand the brackets.}$$
$$4x + 8 - 6x - 2 = x - 2 \qquad \text{Collect similar terms.}$$
$$-2x + 6 = x - 2 \qquad \text{Subtract } x \text{ and 6 from each side.}$$
$$-3x = -8$$
$$x = \frac{8}{3} \qquad \text{Divide both sides by } -3.$$

(iii) Solve $\quad |2x - 3| = 7$

This means

$$2x - 3 = 7 \qquad \text{or} \qquad 2x - 3 = -7$$
$$2x = 10 \qquad\qquad\qquad 2x = -4$$
$$x = 5 \qquad\qquad\qquad x = -2$$

Linear inequalities

These are very similar to linear equations apart from one basic difference.

If you **multiply** or **divide** by a negative number you must reverse the direction of the inequality sign, i.e. > becomes <, ≤ becomes ≥ etc.

Examples

(i) $-2x + 3 > 7$

$\quad\quad -2x > 4$ Subtract 3 from each side.

$\quad\quad\quad x < -2$ Divide both sides by −2.

> Because we have divided by −2 we change the direction of the inequality sign: > becomes <.

(ii) Solve $\quad |x + 3| \leq 4$

This means $\quad x + 3 \leq 4 \quad$ or $\quad -4 \leq x + 3$

$\quad\quad\quad\quad\quad\quad x \leq 1 \quad$ or $\quad -7 \leq x \quad\quad$ Subtract 3

This can be written as one statement $-7 \leq x \leq 1$.

Simultaneous linear equations

Simultaneous linear equations can be solved by three methods.

1 Graphical method

Example

Solve $\ 3x - y = 3\ $ and $\ 2x + 3y = 13$

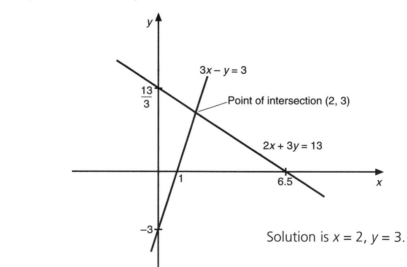

Solution is $x = 2$, $y = 3$.

The weakness of this method is that you do not know whether you have found the exact solutions or just approximate values due to inaccuracies plotting and reading from the graph. You would have to check that they satisfied the original equations to make sure you were right.

2 Substitution

Using the previous example:

$$3x - y = 3 \qquad (1)$$
$$2x + 3y = 13 \qquad (2)$$

From (1) $y = 3x - 3$

Substitute into (2)
$$2x + 3(3x - 3) = 13$$
$$2x + 9x - 9 = 13$$
$$11x = 22$$
$$x = 2$$

and so $\qquad y = 3 \times 2 - 3 = 3 \qquad$ from (1)

3 Elimination

Using the previous example again:

$$3x - y = 3 \qquad (1)$$
$$2x + 3y = 13 \qquad (2)$$
$$9x - 3y = 9 \qquad (1) \times 3 = (4)$$
$$2x + 3y = 13 \qquad (2)$$

Adding (4) and (2)
$$11x = 22$$
$$x = 2$$

$$2 \times 2 + 3y = 13 \qquad \text{using (2)}$$
$$3y = 9$$
$$y = 3$$

Methods 2 and 3 are preferred as they give exact answers. The problem will usually suggest which method to use. Method 2 can be slightly complicated in some cases as the next example shows.

Example

Solve
$$3x + 2y = 13 \qquad (1)$$
$$2x - 7y = -8 \qquad (2)$$

Method 2

$$y = \frac{13 - 3x}{2} \qquad \text{from (1)}$$

$$2x - \frac{7(13 - 3x)}{2} = -8 \qquad \text{substituting into (2)}$$

$$4x - 7(13 - 3x) = -16 \qquad \text{multiplying by 2}$$
$$4x - 91 + 21x = -16$$
$$25x = 75$$
$$x = 3$$

$$y = \frac{13 - 3 \times 3}{2} = 2 \quad \text{from (1)}$$

Be careful of signs.

Method 3

$$6x + 4y = 26 \qquad (3) = (1) \times 2$$
$$6x - 21y = -24 \qquad (4) = (2) \times 3$$

$$25y = 50 \qquad (3) - (4)$$
$$y = 2$$

$$3x + 2 \times 2 = 13 \qquad \text{from (1)}$$
$$3x = 9$$
$$x = 3$$

Quadratic functions

A quadratic function is one of the form $ax^2 + bx + c$ where a, b, c are constants and $a \neq 0$.

Note that a quadratic graph is symmetrical.

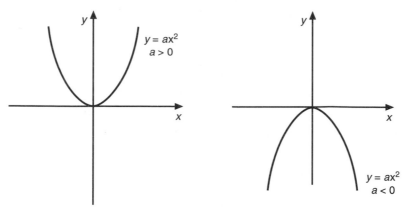

In the graph of $y = ax^2 + bx + c$, the sign of a determines which way up the curve is as in the diagrams above. The bigger $|a|$ is, the steeper the curve is. b has the effect of moving the curve to the left and down ($b > 0$) or to the right and down ($b < 0$). c moves the curve up ($c > 0$) or down ($c < 0$).

Quadratic equations

There are three ways of solving quadratic equations.

$$ax^2 + bx + c = 0, \ a \neq 0.$$

1 Factorisation

$$2x^2 - 7x - 4 = 0$$
$$(2x + 1)(x - 4) = 0$$
$$x = -\frac{1}{2} \ \text{or} \ 4$$

This method is preferred if the quadratic factorises.

2 Completing the square

$$2x^2 - 7x - 4 = 0$$

$$x^2 - \frac{7}{2}x - 2 = 0 \qquad \text{Divide throughout by 2.}$$

$$\left(x - \frac{7}{4}\right)^2 - 2 = \left(\frac{7}{4}\right)^2 \qquad \text{Put half of the quantity in front of the } x \text{ in the bracket and add the square of it to the right-hand side.}$$

$$\left(x - \frac{7}{4}\right)^2 = 2 + \left(\frac{7}{4}\right)^2$$

$$\left(x - \frac{7}{4}\right)^2 = \frac{81}{16}$$

$$x - \frac{7}{4} = \pm\frac{9}{4} \qquad \text{Take the square root of both sides.}$$

$$x = -\frac{1}{2} \ \text{or} \ 4$$

3 Quadratic equation formula

$$x = \frac{-b \pm \sqrt{b^2 - 4ac}}{2a}$$

In our equation $a = 2$ $b = -7$ $c = -4$

$$x = \frac{7 \pm \sqrt{(-7)^2 - 4 \times 2 \times (-4)}}{2 \times 2}$$

$$= \frac{7 \pm \sqrt{81}}{4}$$

$$= -\frac{1}{2} \text{ or } 4$$

Watch the signs.

Learn this carefully, it is often misquoted.

The discriminant

The discriminant $\Delta = b^2 - 4ac$ gives important information about the solutions of a quadratic equation.

Value of Δ	Information given
$\Delta > 0$	There are two distinct solutions.
$\Delta = 0$	There is one repeated solution.
$\Delta < 0$	There are no (real) solutions.
$\Delta =$ a perfect square	The quadratic factorises.

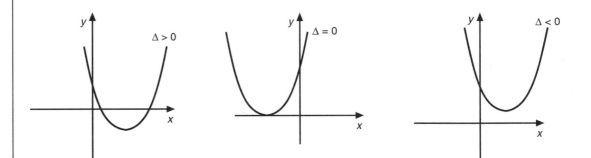

Quadratic equations in disguise

(i) $2x^4 - 7x^2 - 4 = 0$

$(2x^2 + 1)(x^2 - 4) = 0$

$x^2 = -\frac{1}{2}$ or 4

$-\frac{1}{2}$ *Not possible.*

$x = \pm 2$

(ii) $2x - 7 - \frac{4}{x} = 0$

$2x^2 - 7x - 4 = 0$

$(2x + 1)(x - 4) = 0$

$x = -\frac{1}{2}$ or 4

Sketching quadratic graphs

The basic steps involved are:

1 Find out where the curve meets the y-axis by putting $x = 0$.

2 Find out where the curve meets the x-axis by putting $y = 0$ and solving the resulting quadratic equation.

3 Decide which way up the curve is.

It is also possible to use the symmetry of the graph to determine the coordinates of the maximum or minimum points.

1 Find the x-coordinate of the maximum/minimum point by adding the x-coordinates of the points where the curve meets the x-axis and dividing by 2.

2 Find the corresponding y-coordinate by substituting the x-value of the maximum/minimum point into the equation for y.

Example

Sketch the curve $y = 8 - 2x - x^2$.

> When $x = 0$ $y = 8$
> When $y = 0$ $8 - 2x - x^2 = 0$
> $$x^2 + 2x - 8 = 0$$
> $$(x + 4)(x - 2) = 0$$
> $$x = 2 \text{ or } -4$$

The curve is $\cap$ shaped since the coefficient of x^2 is negative.

The x-coordinate of the maximum point is $\dfrac{-4 + 2}{2} = -1$

At this point $y = 8 - 2 \times (-1) - (-1)^2 = 9$

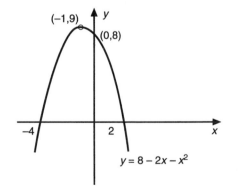

Quadratic inequalities

There are three steps to solving these:

Step 1 Find when the quadratic equals zero (the critical values).
Step 2 Draw a sketch graph.
Step 3 Read off the required ranges.

Examples

Be careful to get the inequality signs right.

(i) $6x^2 - 11x + 4 \leq 0$
$(3x - 4)(2x - 1) = 0$
when $x = \dfrac{4}{3}$ or $\dfrac{1}{2}$

$\dfrac{1}{2} \leq x \leq \dfrac{4}{3}$

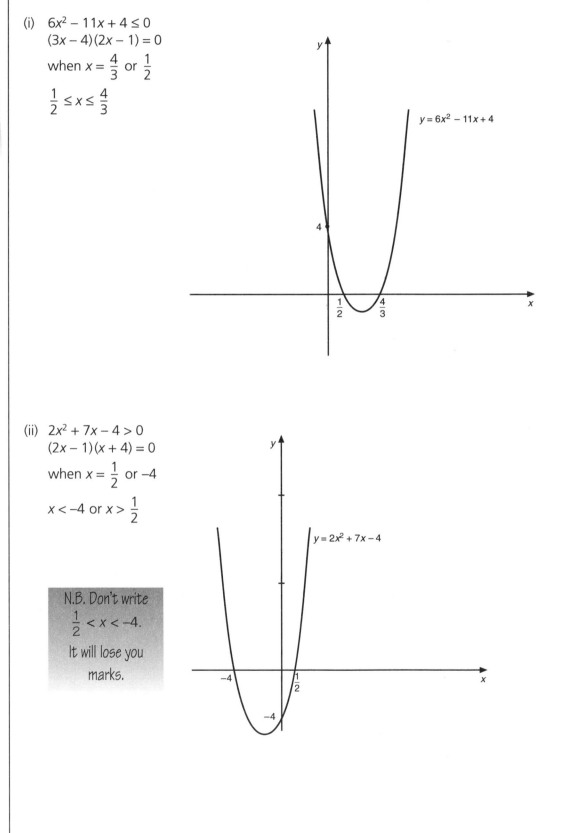

$y = 6x^2 - 11x + 4$

(ii) $2x^2 + 7x - 4 > 0$
$(2x - 1)(x + 4) = 0$
when $x = \dfrac{1}{2}$ or -4

$x < -4$ or $x > \dfrac{1}{2}$

N.B. Don't write $\dfrac{1}{2} < x < -4$.
It will lose you marks.

$y = 2x^2 + 7x - 4$

Cubic inequalities

Use the factor theorem and similar principles to quadratic inequalities.

Example

$2x^3 - 5x^2 - 11x + 14 < 0$

Let $f(x) = 2x^3 - 5x^2 - 11x + 14$
$f(1) = 2 - 5 - 11 + 14 = 0$ so $(x - 1)$ is a factor.
$f(x) = (x - 1)(2x^2 - 3x - 14)$
     $= (x - 1)(x + 2)(2x - 7)$
$f(x) = 0$ when $x = 1, -2$ or $\dfrac{7}{2}$

$f(x) < 0$ when
$x < -2$ or $1 < x < \dfrac{7}{2}$

Simultaneous linear and quadratic equations

Example

$$2x + y = 7 \qquad (1)$$
$$3xy + x^2 = 16 \qquad (2)$$

From (1) $y = 7 - 2x$
Substitute in (2) $3x(7 - 2x) + x^2 = 16$
                 $21x - 6x^2 + x^2 = 16$
                 $5x^2 - 21x + 16 = 0$
                 $(5x - 16)(x - 1) = 0$
$$x = \frac{16}{5} \text{ or } 1$$

From (1) $y = 7 - 2 \times \dfrac{16}{5} = \dfrac{3}{5}$ or $y = 7 - 2 \times 1 = 5$

The solutions are $x = \dfrac{16}{5}$ and $y = \dfrac{3}{5}$ or $x = 1$ and $y = 5$

Make sure you group the solutions as pairs. An x-value with the corresponding y-value.

Questions

1 Solve each of the following equations:

   (a) $\dfrac{3x+2}{5} + \dfrac{x-7}{6} = \dfrac{1}{2}$ (b) $7(x+3) - 6(x+2) = 13x - 7$

   (c) $|3x-4| = 3$

2 Solve each of the following inequalities:

   (a) $6x^2 - 19x - 7 = 0$ (b) $\dfrac{3}{x} - x = 2$

   (c) $4x^4 = x^2 + 18$ (d) $\sqrt{x} + 1 = x$

3 If someone was to walk 1 km/h faster than normal they would take 3 minutes less to travel 1 km. Use an algebraic method to calculate the speed at which they normally walk.

4 Solve each of the following inequalities:

   (a) $6x - 7 < 3x + 5$ (b) $7(3 - x) > 14$
   (c) $|3x + 2| \geq 14$ (d) $6(2x + 1) < 3(7 - 2x)$

5 Solve the following inequalities:

   (a) $12x^2 - 16x - 3 < 0$ (b) $2x^3 + 5x^2 - x - 6 \geq 0$
   (c) $3x(x + 1) < 2x(x - 4) - 10$

6 Solve the following pairs of simultaneous equations:

   (a) $2x + 3y = -15$ (b) $x^2 - 3xy = -26$
       $3x - y = 16$ $3y - 2x = 11$

7 For each of the following quadratic equations state, without first attempting to solve them:

   (i) how many solutions they have,
   (ii) whether they factorise.

       (a) $2x^2 + 3x - 7 = 0$
       (b) $9x^2 - 12x + 4 = 0$
       (c) $35 - x - 6x^2 = 0$
       (d) $8x^2 + 2x + 3 = 0$

8 Sketch the curves

   (a) $y = x^2 - 5x + 4$ (b) $y = 7 + 13x - 2x^2$

   marking on your sketches where the curves meet the coordinate axes and the coordinates of the maximum or minimum point.

Indices and logarithms

When $a^x = b$ we refer to a as the base and x as the power, index (plural, indices) or logarithm.

Laws of indices

- $a^x \times a^y = a^{x+y}$

- $\dfrac{a^x}{a^y} = a^{x-y}$

- $(a^x)^y = a^{xy}$

- $a^{-x} = \dfrac{1}{a^x}$

- $a^{\frac{1}{n}} = \sqrt[n]{a}$

- $a^{\frac{m}{n}} = \sqrt[n]{a^m} = \left(\sqrt[n]{a}\right)^m$

- $a^0 = 1$

- $a^1 = a$

> Make sure you are familiar with the use of the x^y and $x^{1/y}$ (or $\sqrt[y]{x}$) buttons on your calculator as well as the 10^x and e^x buttons.

Examples

(i) $\quad 2^3 \times 2^8 = 2^{3+8} = 2^{11}$

(ii) $\quad 6^7 \div 6^{-3} = 6^{7-(-3)} = 6^{10}$

(iii) $\quad (2^3)^4 = 2^{3\times4} = 2^{12}$

(iv) $\quad 4^{-3} = \dfrac{1}{4^3} = \dfrac{1}{64}$

(v) $\quad 27^{1/3} = \sqrt[3]{27} = 3$

(vi) $\quad 9^{-1/2} = \dfrac{1}{9^{1/2}} = \dfrac{1}{\sqrt{9}} = \dfrac{1}{3}$

(vii) $\quad 16^{5/4} = \left(\sqrt[4]{16}\right)^5 = 2^5 = 32$

(viii) $\quad \left(\dfrac{1}{3}\right)^0 = 1$

(ix) $\quad 27^x = (3^3)^x = 3^{3x} = (3^x)^3$

(x) $\quad (x+1)^{3/2} - (x+1)^{-1/2} = (x+1)^{3/2} - \dfrac{1}{(x+1)^{1/2}}$

$$= \dfrac{(x+1)^{4/2} - 1}{(x+1)^{1/2}}$$

$$= \dfrac{(x+1)^2 - 1}{(x+1)^{1/2}} = \dfrac{x^2 + 2x + 1 - 1}{(x+1)^{1/2}}$$

$$= \dfrac{x^2 + 2x}{\sqrt{x+1}}$$

Other helpful results

- $(ab)^n = a^n b^n$
- $\left(\dfrac{a}{b}\right)^n = \dfrac{a^n}{b^n}$
- $a^x = a^y \Leftrightarrow x = y$

Graph of $y = a^x$

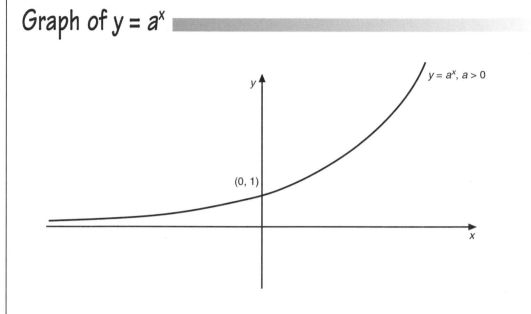

Logarithms

The logarithm equivalent of $a^x = b$

is $\quad \log_a b = x$.

> Read as "the log of b to the base a is x". It means that the power to which you must raise a in order to get b is x.

Logarithms to the base 10 are usually written as log or just lg. These are called **common** logarithms.

Example

$\log_{10} 7 = \log 7 = \lg 7 = 0.845$ (3 significant figures)

Logarithms to the base e (= 2.71828182. . .) are usually written as **ln**. These are called **natural** or **Naperian** logarithms.

Example

$\log_e 4 = \ln 4 = 1.39$ (3 s.f.)

> Make sure you know how to use the log and ln button on your calculator.

Laws of logarithms

- $\log_c ab = \log_c a + \log_c b$ The log of a product is the sum of two logs.

- $\log_c \left(\dfrac{b}{a} \right) = \log_c b - \log_c a$ The log of a quotient is the difference of two logs.

> Note that $\log_c b - \log_c a = \log_c \left(\dfrac{b}{a} \right)$ NOT $\log_c (b - a)$ or $\dfrac{\log_c b}{\log_c a}$. These are both common errors.

- $\log_c a^n = n \log_c a$ The log of a number to a power is the power times the log of the number.

- $\log_c 1 = 0$ (because $c^0 = 1$)

- $\log_c c = 1$ (because $c^1 = c$)

Students often get these wrong. Make sure you don't!

- $\log_c a = \dfrac{1}{\log_a c}$

- $\log_b a = \dfrac{\log_c a}{\log_c b}$

These are known as the **change of base** results.

Notice the following three helpful consequences of these:

- $\log_c \left(\dfrac{1}{a} \right) = \log_c 1 - \log_c a = -\log_c a$

- $\log_c \left(\dfrac{1}{a^n} \right) = \log_c 1 - \log_c a^n = -n \log_c a$

- $\log_c \sqrt[n]{a} = \log_c a^{\frac{1}{n}} = \dfrac{1}{n} \log_c a$

Other helpful results

- $\log_c a = \log_c b \Leftrightarrow a = b$
- $\log (e^x) = x$
- $\log (10^x) = x$
- $e^{\ln x} = x$
- $10^{\log x} = x$

Examples

(i) $\log_4 2 + \log_4 8 = \log_4 (2 \times 8) = \log_4 16 = 2$ since $4^2 = 16$

(ii) $\log x + \log x^2 + \log x^4 = \log x + 2 \log x + 4 \log x = 7 \log x$

(iii) $6 \log_a 2 - 3 \log_a 12 + 5 \log_a 3$

     $= \log_a \left(\dfrac{2^6 \times 3^5}{12^3} \right) = \log_a 9$

(iv) $\log_3 4 = \dfrac{\log 4}{\log 3}$

The change of base rule is very useful.

Graph of $y = \log_n x$

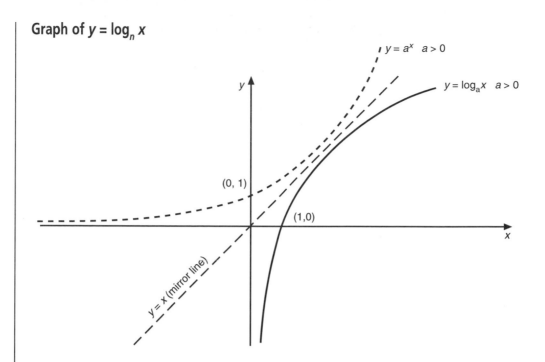

Notice that $y = \log_a x$ is the reflection of $y = a^x$ in the line $y = x$ as one is the inverse of the other.

Notice further that you cannot have the log of a negative number.

See p. 20 for the work on inverse functions.

Solving equations involving indices and logarithms

Examples

(i) Solve $2^x = 3$

$$\ln 2^x = \ln 3 \qquad \text{Taking ln of both sides.}$$
$$x \ln 2 = \ln 3 \qquad \text{Use the laws of logarithms to 'bring the power down'.}$$
$$x = \frac{\ln 3}{\ln 2} = 1.58 \ (3 \text{ s.f.})$$

(ii) Solve $7 \log x = 3$

$$\log x = \frac{3}{7}$$
$$x = 10^{3/7} = 2.68 \ (3 \text{ s.f.}) \qquad \text{Do the inverse of } \log x \text{ which is } 10^x$$

(iii) Solve $e^{2x} - 4e^x - 12 = 0$

Let $y = e^x$

The equation becomes

$$y^2 - 4y - 12 = 0$$
$$(y - 6)(y + 2) = 0$$
$$y = 6 \text{ or } -2$$
$$e^x = 6 \text{ or } -2$$
$$x = \ln 6$$

−2 Not possible – see graph of $y = a^x$.

(iv) Solve $\log_8 x + \log_4 x + \log_2 x = \dfrac{1}{3}$

$$\log_8 x + \log_4 x + \log_2 x = \frac{\log_2 x}{\log_2 8} + \frac{\log_2 x}{\log_2 4} + \log_2 x \qquad \text{Use the change of base results.}$$

$$= \frac{1}{3}\log_2 x + \frac{1}{2}\log_2 x + \log_2 x$$

$$= \frac{11}{6}\log_2 x$$

$$\frac{11}{6}\log_2 x = \frac{1}{3}$$

$$\log_2 x = \frac{2}{11}$$

$$x = 2^{2/11} = 1.13 \text{ (3 s.f.)} \qquad \text{Use the } x^y \text{ button.}$$

(v) Solve $\qquad \log_3 x + \log_x 9 = 3$

$$\log_3 x + \frac{\log_3 9}{\log_3 x} = 3$$

$$\log_3 x + \frac{2}{\log_3 x} = 3$$

$$(\log_3 x)^2 + 2 = 3\log_3 x$$

$$(\log_3 x)^2 - 3\log_3 x + 2 = 0$$

$$(\log_3 x - 1)(\log_3 x - 2) = 0$$

$$\log_3 x = 1 \text{ or } 2$$

$$x = 3^1 \text{ or } 3^2$$

$$x = 3 \text{ or } 9$$

(vi) Solve simultaneously $2\log_x y = 1$

$$xy = 64$$

$$\log_x y^2 = 1$$

$$y^2 = x^1 = x$$

Substituting into the second equation for x in terms of y

$$y^2 \cdot y = 64$$

$$y^3 = 64$$

$$y = 4$$

$$x = y^2 = 16$$

Questions

1 Simplify fully:

(a) $125^{-1/3}$

(b) $\left(\dfrac{1}{4}\right)^{-3/2}$

(c) $\dfrac{y^{1/6}\, y^{-2/3}}{y^{1/2}}$

(d) $\dfrac{(x-1)^{1/2} + (x-1)^{-1/2}}{(x-1)^{1/2}}$

(e) $\log_{16} 8$

(f) $e^{\ln 7}$

(g) $\log 2 + \log 12 - \log 4$

(h) $\dfrac{1}{2} \log 25$

(i) $\log (x^2 - 1) - \log (x + 1)$

2 Sketch the graphs of:

(a) $y = 3^x$

(b) $y = \log_3 x$

Explain how the graphs are related.

3 Solve each of the following equations:

(a) $6^x = 7^{2x-1}$

(b) $2(3^{2x}) - 5(3^x) + 2 = 0$

(c) $16^x - 6(4^x) - 16 = 0$

(d) $\log_3 x - 12 \log_x 3 = 1$

4 Solve the following pairs of simultaneous equations:

(a) $\log_2 y + \log_2 x = 5$

$\log_2 \left(\dfrac{y}{x}\right) = 1$

(b) $\log(x + y) = 0$

$2 \log x = \log(y + 1)$

5 Solve the equation $8^x - 2(4^x) - 5(2^x) + 6 = 0$

Sequences and series

- A **sequence** is a list of numbers obeying a rule.

- The nth term in the list is given the symbol u_n.

- The sum of the terms in a sequence is called a **series**.

- The sum of the first n terms of a sequence is given the symbol S_n, i.e. $S_n = u_1 + u_2 + u_3 \cdots + u_n$.

- A **finite** series has a **finite** number of terms.

- An **infinite** series has an **infinite** number of terms.

- A sequence is **convergent** if $u_n \to l$ (a fixed number) as $n \to \infty$.

- A sequence is **divergent** if $u_n \to \infty$ or $u_n \to -\infty$ as $n \to \infty$.

- A sequence which is not convergent or divergent is said to be **oscillating**.

- A **periodic** sequence is one which repeats itself.

Examples

Type of sequence	Example
Convergent	$\frac{1}{2}, \frac{2}{3}, \frac{3}{4}, \frac{4}{5}, \ldots$ (converges to 1)
Divergent	2, 4, 8, 16, 32, …
Oscillating	1, –3, 9, –27, 81, …
Periodic	1, 2, 3, 1, 2, 3, 1, 2, 3, …

Sequences can be defined **explicitly** by giving a formula for the general term,

For example, $u_n = (n - 2)^3 + 1$

giving
$$u_1 = (1 - 2)^3 + 1 = 0$$
$$u_2 = (2 - 2)^3 + 1 = 1$$
$$u_3 = (3 - 2)^3 + 1 = 2$$
$$u_4 = (4 - 2)^3 + 1 = 9 \quad \text{etc.}$$

or **implicitly** by **recurrence relationships** and a starting value.

For example, $u_n = \frac{1}{2}u_{n-1}^2, \qquad u_0 = 1$

giving
$$u_1 = \frac{1}{2}u_0^2 = \frac{1}{2} \times 1^2 = \frac{1}{2}$$

$$u_2 = \frac{1}{2}u_1^2 = \frac{1}{2}\left(\frac{1}{2}\right)^2 = \frac{1}{8}$$

$$u_3 = \frac{1}{2}u_2^2 = \frac{1}{2}\left(\frac{1}{8}\right)^2 = \frac{1}{128} \quad \text{etc.}$$

Sigma notation

A $\sum$ symbol is used to represent summation.

$$\sum_{i-1}^{n} u_i \text{ means } u_1 + u_2 + u_3 + \cdots + u_n.$$

Example

A finite series
$$\sum_{i=1}^{8} \frac{1}{i^2 + 1} = \frac{1}{1^2 + 1} + \frac{1}{2^2 + 1} + \frac{1}{3^2 + 1} + \cdots + \frac{1}{8^2 + 1}$$
$$= \frac{1}{2} + \frac{1}{5} + \frac{1}{10} + \cdots + \frac{1}{65}.$$

An infinite series
$$\sum_{i=1}^{\infty} \frac{1}{i} = \frac{1}{1} + \frac{1}{2} + \frac{1}{3} + \frac{1}{4} + \cdots.$$

Arithmetic sequences

An **arithmetic sequence** is one of the form

a, $a + d$, $a + 2d$, $a + 3d$, ...

where d is called the **common difference** and a is the first term.

> These properties are important.

> l is the final term.

- $u_n = a + (n - 1)d$ is the nth term.
- $S_n = \frac{n}{2}\left(2a + (n - 1)d\right) = \frac{n}{2}\left(a + l\right)$ is the sum of the first n terms.
- $u_n - u_{n-1} = d$
- $S_n = S_{n-1} + u_n$

> These two properties some times make a question much easier than using the formulae u_n and S_n.

Examples

(i) The fifth term of an arithmetic progression is −1 and the sum of the first twenty terms is −240. Find the third term.

$$\left.\begin{array}{l} u_5 = a + (5 - 1)d = -1 \\ S_{20} = \frac{20}{2}\left\{2a + (20 - 1)d\right\} = -240 \end{array}\right\} \text{give}$$

$$\begin{array}{ll} a + 4d = -1 & (1) \\ 2a + 19d = -24 & (2) \\ 2a + 8d = -2 & (1) \times 2 = (3) \\ \hline \end{array}$$

subtract
$$\begin{array}{ll} 11d = -22 & (2) - (3) \\ d = -2 & \end{array}$$

substitute in (1)
$$\begin{array}{l} a - 8 = -1 \\ a = 7 \end{array}$$

Third term
$$\begin{aligned} u_3 &= a + 2d \\ &= 7 + 2 \times (-2) \\ &= 3 \end{aligned}$$

(ii) A sequence is such that $S_n = n^2 + 3n$, $n \in \mathbb{Z}_+$. Show that the terms of this sequence are in arithmetic progression.

$$\begin{aligned} u_n = S_n - S_{n-1} &= n^2 + 3n - [(n - 1)^2 + 3(n - 1)] \\ &= n^2 + 3n - [n^2 - 2n + 1 + 3n - 3] \\ u_n &= 2n + 2 \\ u_n - u_{n-1} &= 2n + 2 - [2(n - 1) + 2] \\ &= 2n + 2 - [2n - 2 + 2] \\ &= 2 \end{aligned}$$

> Replacing n by $n - 1$ in the formulae for S_n and u_n give S_{n-1} and u_{n-1} respectively.

As this is a constant the terms are in arithmetic progression.

Geometric sequences

A **geometric sequence** is one of the form:

a, ar, ar^2, ar^3, ...

where r is called the **common ratio** and a is the first term.

- $u_n = ar^{n-1}$ is the nth term.

- $S_n = \dfrac{a(1 - r^n)}{(1 - r)} = \dfrac{a(r^n - 1)}{(r - 1)}$ is the sum of the first n terms.

- $\dfrac{u_n}{u_{n-1}} = r$

- $S_n = S_{n-1} + u_n$

If $-1 < r < 1$ then the geometric series has a sum to infinity, S_∞, given by

$S_\infty = \dfrac{a}{1 - r}$.

Make sure you are quite sure which formulae are for geometric sequences and which are for arithmetic sequences – getting muddled is very common.

Examples

(i) The sum of the first three terms of a geometric sequence is 8 and the sum of the first six terms is 12. Find the common ratio.

$$S_6 = \frac{a(1 - r^6)}{(1 - r)} = 12 \qquad (1)$$

$$S_3 = \frac{a(1 - r^3)}{(1 - r)} = 8 \qquad (2)$$

$$\frac{a(1 - r^6)}{(1 - r)} \; \frac{(1 - r)}{a(1 - r^3)} = \frac{12}{8} \qquad (1) \div (2)$$

$$1 + r^3 = \frac{12}{8} \qquad\qquad \text{Since } 1 - r^6 = (1 - r^3)(1 + r^3)$$
$$\text{(difference of two squares)}$$

$$r^3 = \frac{1}{2}$$

$$r = \frac{1}{\sqrt[3]{2}}$$

(ii) The first, second and fourth terms of an arithmetic progression are also consecutive terms in a geometric progression. Given that the ninth term of the arithmetic progression is 12, find the common difference of the arithmetic progression and the common ratio of the geometric progression.

For the arithmetic progression

$$u_1 = a \qquad u_2 = a + d \qquad u_4 = a + 3d$$

and $u_9 = a + 8d = 12 \qquad (1)$

We know that $\dfrac{a + d}{a} = \dfrac{a + 3d}{a + d}$

Since $\dfrac{u_2}{u_1} = \dfrac{u_4}{u_2} = r,$ the common ratio of the geometric progression.

So $(a + d)^2 = a(a + 3d)$
$$a^2 + 2ad + d^2 = a^2 + 3ad$$
$$d^2 - ad = 0$$
$$d(d - a) = 0$$

42 MATHEMATICS REVISION NOTES

Now $d \neq 0$ for an arithmetic progression

so $d = a$

From (1) above $d + 8d = 12$

i.e. the common difference, $d = \dfrac{4}{3}$

and the common ratio, $r = \dfrac{a+d}{a} = \dfrac{\frac{4}{3} + \frac{4}{3}}{\frac{4}{3}} = 2$

Binomial expansions

If $n \in \mathbb{Z}_+$ (positive integers)

$$(1 + x)^n = 1 + \binom{n}{1} x + \binom{n}{2} x^2 + \binom{n}{3} x^3 + \cdots + \binom{n}{r} x^r + \cdots + x^n,$$

where $\quad \dbinom{n}{r} = \dfrac{n!}{r!\,(n-r)!} \quad$ and $\quad r! = r(r-1)(r-2) \cdots 3 \times 2 \times 1.$

Note that $\dbinom{n}{r}$ is sometimes written as ^nC_r.

This is called a series in **ascending powers** of x as the powers are increasing.

The expansion for $(1 + x)^n$ can be simplified to

$$(1 + x)^n = 1 + nx + n(n-1)\,\frac{x^2}{2!} + n(n-1)(n-2)\,\frac{x^3}{3!} + \cdots$$
$$+ n(n-1)(n-2) \cdots (n-r+1)\,\frac{x^r}{r!} + \cdots x^n.$$

It can also be shown that

$$(a + b)^n = a^n + \binom{n}{1} a^{n-1}b + \binom{n}{2} a^{n-2}b^2 + \cdots + \binom{n}{r} a^{n-r}b^r + \cdots + b^n$$
$$= a^n + n\,a^{n-1}b + \frac{n(n-1)}{2!}\,a^{n-2}b^2 + \cdots + \frac{n(n-1)(n-2)\cdots(n-r+1)}{r!}\,a^{n-r}b^r$$
$$+ \cdots + b^n.$$

Example

$$(3 + 2x)^7 = 3^7 + \binom{7}{1} 3^6\,(2x) + \binom{7}{2} 3^5\,(2x)^2 + \cdots + (2x)^7$$
$$= 2187 + 10206x + 20412x^2 + 22680x^3$$
$$+ 15120x^4 + 6048x^5 + 1344x^6 + 128x^7$$

A common mistake is to fail to put $(2x)$ in brackets.

If $n \in \mathbb{R}$ and $|x| < 1$ it can be shown that

$$(1 + x)^n = 1 + nx + \frac{n(n-1)}{2!}\,x^2 + \frac{n(n-1)(n-2)}{3!}\,x^3 + \cdots + \frac{(n-1)(n-2)\cdots(n-r+1)}{r!}\,x^r + \cdots$$

giving an **infinite series**.

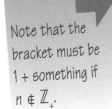

Note that the bracket must be 1 + something if $n \notin \mathbb{Z}_+$.

Examples

(i) $(1-3x)^{-1/2} = 1 + \left(-\dfrac{1}{2}\right)(-3x) + \dfrac{\left(-\frac{1}{2}\right)\left(-\frac{3}{2}\right)(-3x)^2}{2!} + \dfrac{\left(-\frac{1}{2}\right)\left(-\frac{3}{2}\right)\left(-\frac{5}{2}\right)(-3x)^2}{3!} + \cdots$

Again make sure you are using powers of (-3x).

$= 1 + \dfrac{3}{2}x + \dfrac{27}{8}x^2 + \dfrac{135}{16}x^3 + \cdots$

(ii) $(2+x)^{1/3} = \left[2\left(1+\dfrac{x}{2}\right)\right]^{1/3}$

These two steps are important so make sure you understand them.

$= 2^{1/3}\left(1+\dfrac{x}{2}\right)^{1/3}$

$= 2^{1/3}\left[1 + \dfrac{1}{3}\left(\dfrac{x}{2}\right) + \dfrac{\left(\frac{1}{3}\right)\left(-\frac{2}{3}\right)\left(\frac{x}{2}\right)^2}{2!} + \dfrac{\left(\frac{1}{3}\right)\left(-\frac{2}{3}\right)\left(-\frac{5}{3}\right)\left(\frac{x}{2}\right)^3}{3!} + \cdots\right]$

$= 2^{1/3}\left[1 + \dfrac{1}{6}x - \dfrac{1}{24}x^2 + \dfrac{5}{648}x^3 - \cdots\right]$

This expansion is valid for $\left|\dfrac{x}{2}\right| < 1$, *i.e.* $|x| < 2 \ (-2 < x < 2)$.

Approximations using binomial expansions

Approximations can be obtained using the binomial expansion.

Example

Find an approximate value for $0.997^{-1/2}$.

Using the expansion of $(1-3x)^{-1/2}$ with $x = 0.001$ gives an approximation to $0.997^{-1/2}$

$0.997^{-1/2} = (1-0.003)^{-1/2} = (1-3(0.001))^{-1/2}$

So $0.997^{-1/2} \approx 1 + \dfrac{3}{2}(0.001) + \dfrac{27}{8}(0.001)^2 + \dfrac{135}{16}(0.001)^3$ from the example above

$= 1.001503383$

Care should be given to choosing an appropriate degree of accuracy for the answer. This value is actually correct to at least 8 decimal places.

Maclaurin series

It can be shown that many functions can be expressed as an infinite series in ascending powers of x. In this case the Maclaurin series expansion of $f(x)$ is given by

$$f(x) = f(0) + f'(0)x + \dfrac{f''(0)}{2!}x^2 + \dfrac{f'''(0)}{3!}x^3 + \cdots + \dfrac{f^r(0)}{r!}x^r + \cdots$$

where $f'(x) = \dfrac{d(f(x))}{dx}$; $f''(x) = \dfrac{d^2}{dx^2}(f(x))$; $f^r(x) = \dfrac{d^r}{dx^r}(f(x))$ etc.

Some commonly used series expansions are as follows:

- $$e^x = 1 + x + \frac{x^2}{2!} + \frac{x^3}{3!} + \frac{x^4}{4!} + \cdots$$ 　　　Valid for $x \in \mathbb{R}$

- $$\sin x = x - \frac{x^3}{3!} + \frac{x^5}{5!} - \frac{x^7}{7!} + \frac{x^9}{9!} - \cdots$$ 　　　Valid for $x \in \mathbb{R}$ when x is in radians.

- $$\cos x = 1 - \frac{x^2}{2!} + \frac{x^4}{4!} - \frac{x^6}{6!} + \frac{x^8}{8!} - \cdots$$ 　　　Valid for $x \in \mathbb{R}$ when x is in radians.

- $$\ln(1 + x) = x - \frac{x^2}{2} + \frac{x^3}{3} - \frac{x^4}{4} + \frac{x^5}{5} - \frac{x^6}{6} + \cdots$$ 　　　Valid for $-1 < x \le 1$

These series can be combined in many ways.

Example

Express $e^{2x} \cos 3x$ as a series in ascending powers of x up to and including the term in x^2.

$$e^{2x} = 1 + (2x) + \frac{(2x)^2}{2!} + \cdots = 1 + 2x + 2x^2 + \cdots$$

> Replace x by $2x$ in the expansion of e^x.

$$\cos 3x = 1 - \frac{(3x)^2}{2!} + \cdots = 1 - \frac{9x^2}{2} + \cdots$$

> Replace x by $3x$ in the expansion of $\cos x$.

$$e^{2x} \cos 3x = (1 + 2x + 2x^2 + \cdots)\left(1 - \frac{9x^2}{2} + \cdots\right)$$

$$= 1 \qquad\quad - \frac{9x^2}{2}$$
$$\quad\;\; + 2x$$
$$\qquad\quad + 2x^2$$

$$= 1 + 2x - \frac{13x^2}{2} + \cdots$$

> Multiply each term in the second bracket by each term in the first ignoring anything with a power higher than 2.

Laying the working out this way can help the adding up.

Questions

1 For each of the following sequences state whether they are convergent, divergent, oscillating or periodic:

   (a) $2, 4, 8, 16, \ldots$

   (b) $\dfrac{1}{2}, -\dfrac{3}{4}, \dfrac{7}{8}, -\dfrac{15}{16}, \dfrac{31}{32}, \ldots$

   (c) $1, 0, -1, 0, 1, 0, -1, 0, 1, \ldots$

   (d) $1, -3, 9, -27, 81, \ldots$

   (e) $0, \dfrac{1}{2}, \dfrac{3}{4}, \dfrac{7}{8}, \dfrac{15}{16}, \dfrac{31}{32}, \dfrac{63}{64}, \ldots$

2 Write down the next four terms of the sequence given by $u_{n+1} = 3u_n + \dfrac{1}{u_n}$, $u_0 = 3$, giving each answer correct to 3 decimal places.

3 Evaluate $\displaystyle\sum_{n=1}^{6} \sin\left(\dfrac{n\pi}{6}\right)$ giving your answer to 3 significant figures.

4 The sum of the first 20 terms of an arithmetic progression is −145 and the sum of the first 38 terms is −788.5. Find the seventh term of the arithmetic progression.

5 The first term of an arithmetic progression is 7, the last term is 43 and the sum of the terms of the progression is 250. Find the number of terms.

6 The first term of a geometric progression is 1 and the sum of the first 3 terms is 13/9. Find the two possible values of the common ratio, state the value of the common ratio which causes the geometric progression to have a sum to infinity and find this sum to infinity.

7 Find the series expansions for each of the following giving your expansion up to and including the term in x^3.

   (a) $(3 - 2x)^5$

   (b) $\dfrac{1}{\sqrt[4]{3 - x}}$

   (c) $\sin 4x$

   (d) $(x - 1) \ln (1 + 2x)$

   (e) $\ln (2 - 3x)$

   (f) $2 \sin x \cos x$

   State the range of values for which each series expansion is valid.

8 Use a suitable series expansion to find an approximate value for $\sqrt{1.02}$ correct to 5 decimal places.

Coordinate geometry

Distance between two points

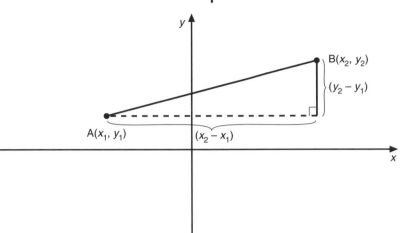

The distance AB between two points $A(x_1, y_1)$ and $B(x_2, y_2)$ is given by

$$AB = \sqrt{(x_2 - x_1)^2 + (y_2 - y_1)^2}.$$

Example

Find the distance between $(-6, 3)$ and $(3, 1)$.

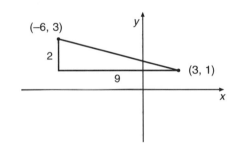

$$\text{Distance} = \sqrt{(3 - (-6))^2 + (1 - 3)^2}$$
$$= \sqrt{9^2 + 2^2} = \sqrt{85}$$

Watch out for sign slips.

Make sure you are consistent with the order.

Gradient of a straight line

The **gradient** of the straight line AB is given by

$$m = \frac{y_2 - y_1}{x_2 - x_1} \qquad \text{i.e.} \quad \frac{\text{difference in } y \text{ values}}{\text{difference in } x \text{ values}}.$$

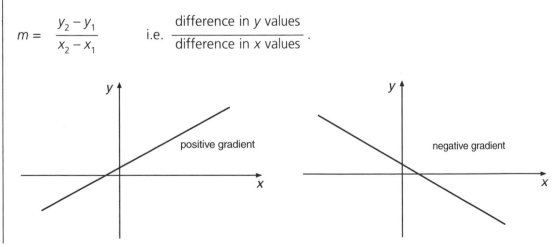

positive gradient

negative gradient

Example

Find the gradient of the line joining (–8, 4) and (4, 1).

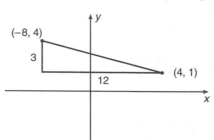

$$\text{Gradient} = \frac{1-4}{4-(-8)} = -\frac{3}{12} = -\frac{1}{4}$$

Equation of a straight line

The equation of any straight line can always be written in the form

$$y = mx + c$$

where m is the gradient and c is the y-intercept (the point where the line meets the y-axis).

In order to find the equation of a straight line we need to know:

- The direction of the line.

- One point on the line.

This information can come from:

- Two points on the line, or

- One point on the line and the gradient.

Example

Find the equation of the line through (2, 7) and (6, 19).

The gradient is $\frac{19-7}{6-2} = \frac{12}{4} = 3$.

Choose whichever method you prefer.

We can adopt two approaches:

1 We know $y = 3x + c$ and that $y = 7$ when $x = 2$

   $\therefore 7 = 3 \times 2 + c \Rightarrow c = 1 \Rightarrow y = 3x + 1$

2 If (x, y) is any point on the line:

   $\frac{y-7}{x-2} = 3 \Rightarrow y - 7 = 3(x-2) \Rightarrow y - 7 = 3x - 6 \Rightarrow y = 3x + 1$.

Parallel and perpendicular lines

If L_1 and L_2 are the lines with equations $y = m_1x + c_1$ and $y = m_2x + c_2$, respectively, then

- L_1 and L_2 are parallel if and only if $m_1 = m_2$.

- L_1 and L_2 intersect if and only if $m_1 \neq m_2$.

- L_1 and L_2 are perpendicular if and only if

  $m_1m_2 = -1$ i.e. $m_2 = \frac{-1}{m_1}$.

Example

The lines L_1, L_2 and L_3 have equations $2y = 4x + 3$, $y - 2x = 9$ and $2y + x = 7$, respectively. Show that L_1 and L_2 are parallel and that L_1 and L_3 are perpendicular.

$L_1 \quad y = 2x + \dfrac{3}{2}$

$L_2 \quad y = 2x + 9$

$L_3 \quad y = -\dfrac{1}{2}x + \dfrac{7}{2}$

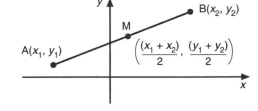

Arrange in the form
$y = mx + c$ first.

Gradient of L_1 = Gradient of L_2 = 2 so L_1 is parallel to L_2.

Gradient of L_1 × Gradient L_3 = $2 \times -\dfrac{1}{2} = -1$ so L_1 is perpendicular to L_3.

The angle between two straight lines

The acute angle, θ, between $y = m_1x + c_1$ and $y = m_2x + c_2$ is given by

$$\tan \theta = \left| \frac{m_1 - m_2}{1 + m_1 m_2} \right|.$$

Mid-points of straight lines

The mid-point $M(x_m, y_m)$ of $A(x_1, y_1)$ and $B(x_2, y_2)$ is given by

- $(x_m, y_m) = \left(\dfrac{x_1 + x_2}{2}, \dfrac{y_1 + y_2}{2} \right).$

Example

The mid-point of (–3, 9) and (6, 13) is

$$\left(\frac{-3 + 6}{2}, \frac{9 + 13}{2} \right) = \left(\frac{3}{2}, 11 \right).$$

Watch for sign errors.

Extension to three-dimensional coordinates

If P and Q have coordinates (x_1, y_1, z_1) and (x_2, y_2, z_2), respectively, then:

- The distance PQ is given by $\sqrt{(x_2 - x_1)^2 + (y_2 - y_1)^2 + (z_2 - z_1)^2}$.

- The mid-point M of PQ has coordinates $\left(\dfrac{x_1 + x_2}{2}, \dfrac{y_1 + y_2}{2}, \dfrac{z_1 + z_2}{2} \right).$

Example

Find the distance between P (0, –3, 7) and Q (1, 1, –2) and the coordinates of the mid-point M of PQ.

$$PQ = \sqrt{(1 - 0)^2 + (1 - (-3))^2 + (-2 - 7)^2} = \sqrt{1^2 + 4^2 + 9^2} = \sqrt{98} = 7\sqrt{2}$$

$$M \text{ is } \left(\frac{0 + 1}{2}, \frac{-3 + 1}{2}, \frac{7 + (-2)}{2} \right) = \left(\frac{1}{2}, -1, \frac{5}{2} \right)$$

Curve sketching

Some useful tips to help with the sketching of the curve $y = f(x)$:

1 See if the curve is related to familiar curves, e.g. quadratics; cubics; exponentials (e.g. e^x, 2^x, etc.); logarithmic graphs (e.g. $\ln x$ etc.); trigonometric graphs (e.g. $\sin x$, $\cos x$, $\tan x$, $\operatorname{cosec} x$, $\sec x$, $\cot x$) by the transformations outlined in topic 2.

2 Find where the curve meets the y-axis (put $x = 0$).

3 Find where the curve meets the x-axis (put $y = 0$ and solve the resulting equation).

4 Find and classify any stationary points (i.e. find where $\dfrac{dy}{dx} = 0$ and decide whether these are maximum points, minimum points or points of inflexion).

5 See what happens as $x \to \pm \infty$.

6 Find x values for which $f(x)$ is not defined.

7 If you are sketching a curve given by parametric equations substitute a few values of the parameter in and plot a few points.

It may of course be possible to eliminate the parameter and use points 1–6 above!

Example

Sketch the graph $y = x\,e^{-x}$.

Considering the suggestions listed above:

1 Not relevant.

2, 3 When $x = 0$, $\quad y = 0 \times e^0 = 0$.

4 $\dfrac{dy}{dx} = 1 \times e^{-x} - x\,e^{-x} = (1-x)e^{-x};$ $\qquad \dfrac{dy}{dx} = 0$ when $x = 1$, $y = e^{-1}$.

$\dfrac{d^2y}{dx^2} = -e^{-x} + (1-x)(-e^{-x}) = (x-2)\,e^{-x} \Rightarrow \left.\dfrac{d^2y}{dx^2}\right|_{x=1} = -e^{-1} < 0$

This means that $(1, e^{-1})$ is a maximum point.

5 As $x \to \infty \qquad y \to 0$
   As $x \to \infty \qquad y \to -\infty$

6 No points for which $f(x)$ is not defined.

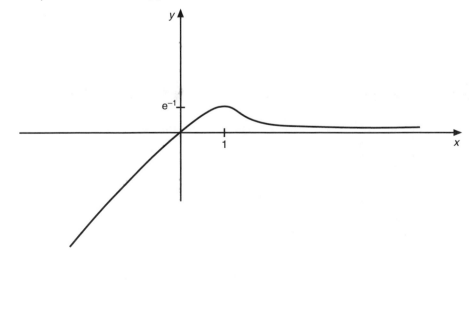

Reducing relationship to linear form

If x and y satisfy the relationship $f(y) = mg(x) + c$ then plotting $Y = f(y)$ against $X = g(x)$ gives a straight line with gradient m and Y intercept C.

Original relationship	Plot	Against	Gradient	Y intercept
$y = ax^2 + b$	$Y = y$	$X = x^2$	a	b
$y^2 = ax^3 + b$	$Y = y^2$	$X = x^3$	a	b
$\sin y = \dfrac{a}{x} + b$	$Y = \sin y$	$X = \dfrac{1}{x}$	a	b
$y = ax^2 + bx$	$Y = \dfrac{y}{x}$	$X = x$	a	b
$\dfrac{1}{x} + \dfrac{1}{y} = \dfrac{1}{b}$	$Y = \dfrac{1}{y}$	$X = \dfrac{1}{x}$	-1	$\dfrac{1}{b}$
$y = ax^n$	$Y = \ln y$	$X = \ln x$	n	$\ln a$
$y = ab^x$	$Y = \ln y$	$X = x$	$\ln b$	$\ln a$

Example

It is believed that x and y follow a relationship of the form $y^2 = ax^n$. Use the data in the table below to demonstrate that this is approximately true and find a and n to 1 decimal place.

x	2.31	2.65	3.87	4.91	6.25	10.37
y	1.97	2.17	2.81	3.37	3.96	5.60

If the relationship is true so plot

$\ln y^2 = \ln a + n \ln x$
$\ln y^2$ against $\ln x$.

$\ln x$	0.84	0.97	1.35	1.59	1.83	2.34
$\ln y^2$	1.36	1.55	2.07	2.43	2.75	3.45

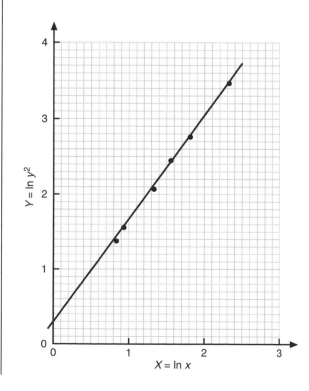

Points lie approximately on a straight line so relationship is approximately true.

$Y = \ln y^2$ intercept $= \ln a = 0.3$
$$a = e^{0.3} \approx 1.3$$

$$n = \text{gradient} = \frac{3 - 0.3}{2 - 0} \approx 1.4$$

Questions

1   Find the distance between (6, 7, –3) and (2, –2, 1).

2   Find the mid-point of (6, –2, 9) and (–2, 8, 4).

3   Find the distance between A(1, 7) and the mid-point M of P(3, –7) and Q(7, 1).

4   Decide for each of the following pairs of lines whether:
    (i)   they meet,
    (ii) they are parallel,
    (iii) they are perpendicular.

    (a) $3y = 2x + 4$ and $3y = -2x - 7$.
    (b) $2y - x = 7$ and $4y = 2x - 12$.
    (c) $x - 3y = 4$ and $3y + 9x = 4$.

5   Find the equation of the line which:
    (a) has gradient –7 and goes through (3, 2).
    (b) goes through (6, 1) and (2, 13).
    (c) meets the x-axis at –3 and the y-axis at 5.

6   Find the x- and y-intercepts for the line $2x + 3y = 5$.

7   Find the acute angle between the lines
    $y = 2x + 7$ and $2y + 3x = -3$.

8   Sketch the curve $y = \dfrac{x}{x-1}$.

9   Sketch the curve $y = 2 \sin 3x + 1$ for the range $0 \le x \le 2\pi$.

10 It is believed that y and x satisfy a relationship of the form $xy = 7 + x$. An appropriate straight line graph of $Y = f(y)$ against $X = g(x)$ is plotted and a sketch is given below.

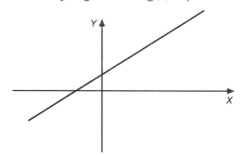

    (a) Write down what $f(y)$ and $g(x)$ might be.
    (b) Write down what you would expect (i) the Y intercept, and (ii) the gradient to be.

11 It is believed that x and y satisfy a relationship of the form $y = ab^x$. A sample of data is given in the table below.

x	2.39	4.17	7.23	8.19	10.2
y	2.51	9.62	17.62	20.21	25.73

    (a) Draw up an appropriate table to draw a straight line graph.

    On the straight line graph the Y intercept is 0.69 and the gradient is 0.095. Find

    (b) the value of a
    (c) the value of b

    giving your answers to 2 significant figures.

Trigonometry

Units of measurement

It is important to know when to work in **degrees** and when to work in **radians**.

Differentiation or **integration always** requires you to work in **radians**.

You need to be able to convert from degrees to radians and vice versa fluently. Some equivalents are given below.

You are strongly advised to learn these.

Degrees	Radians	Degrees	Radians	Degrees	Radians
360	2π	60	$\pi/3$	30	$\pi/6$
180	π	120	$2\pi/3$	150	$5\pi/6$
90	$\pi/2$	240	$4\pi/3$	210	$7\pi/6$
45	$\pi/4$	300	$5\pi/3$	330	$11\pi/6$

Trigonometry in right-angled triangles

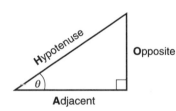

$$\sin \theta = \frac{O}{H} \qquad \cos \theta = \frac{A}{H} \qquad \tan \theta = \frac{O}{A}$$

The terms opposite and adjacent are relative to a particular angle.

Some useful identities are:

- $\cos(90 - \theta) = \sin \theta$
- $\sin(90 - \theta) = \cos \theta$
- $\tan(90 - \theta) = \dfrac{1}{\tan \theta}$

Special values of sin, cos and tan

θ	$\sin \theta$	$\cos \theta$	$\tan \theta$
0°	0	1	0
30°	$\dfrac{1}{2}$	$\dfrac{\sqrt{3}}{2}$	$\dfrac{1}{\sqrt{3}}$
45°	$\dfrac{1}{\sqrt{2}}$	$\dfrac{1}{\sqrt{2}}$	1
60°	$\dfrac{\sqrt{3}}{2}$	$\dfrac{1}{2}$	$\sqrt{3}$
90°	1	0	∞

Graphs of sine, cosine and tangent

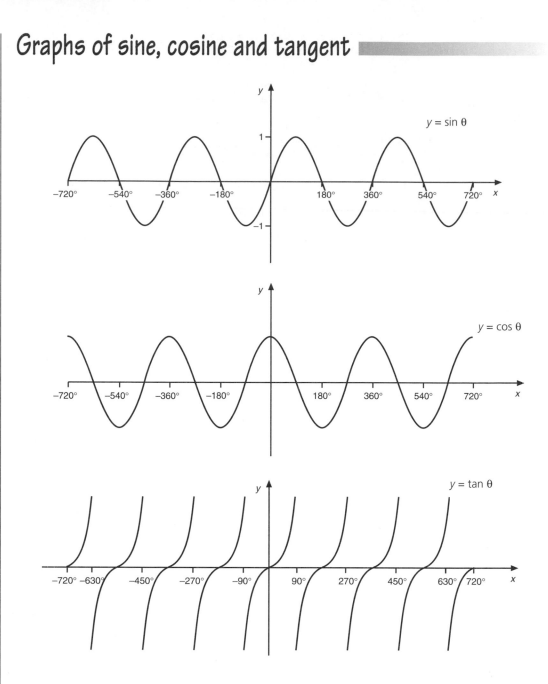

$y = \sin \theta$

$y = \cos \theta$

$y = \tan \theta$

Observations

- $\sin \theta$ and $\cos \theta$ are periodic with period 360° (2π radians).
- $\tan \theta$ is periodic with period 180° (π radians).
- $\sin \theta$ is an odd function, i.e. $\sin(-\theta) = -\sin \theta$.
- $\sin(180 - \theta) = \sin \theta$.
- $\cos \theta$ is an even function, i.e. $\cos(-\theta) = \cos \theta$.
- $\cos(180 - \theta) = -\cos \theta$.
- $\tan \theta$ is an odd function, i.e. $\tan(-\theta) = -\tan \theta$.
- $\tan(180 - \theta) = -\tan \theta$.

For $0 \leq \theta < 360°$

- The maximum value of $\sin \theta$ is 1 when $\theta = 90°$.
- The minimum value of $\sin \theta$ is −1 when $\theta = 270°$.
- The maximum value of $\cos \theta$ is 1 when $\theta = 0°$.
- The minimum value of $\cos \theta$ is −1 when $\theta = 180°$.

Solving simple equations

Examples

Always use the symmetry of sketch graphs to help you.

(i) $\sin x = -0.3$ $0 \leq x \leq 360°$
$x = 180 + 17.5$ or $360 - 17.5$

               $\sin^{-1} 0.3$

$x = 197.5°$ or $342.5°$

The question makes it clear that answers in radians are needed.

(ii) $\cos x = 0.2$ $-\pi \leq x \leq \pi$
$x = \pm 1.37$

        $\cos^{-1} (0.2)$

(iii) $\tan x = 0.75$ $-180° \leq x \leq 360°$
$x = 36.9, \; 36.9 + 180, \; 36.9 - 180$

        $\tan^{-1} 0.75$

$x = 36.9°, \; 216.9°, \; -143.1°$

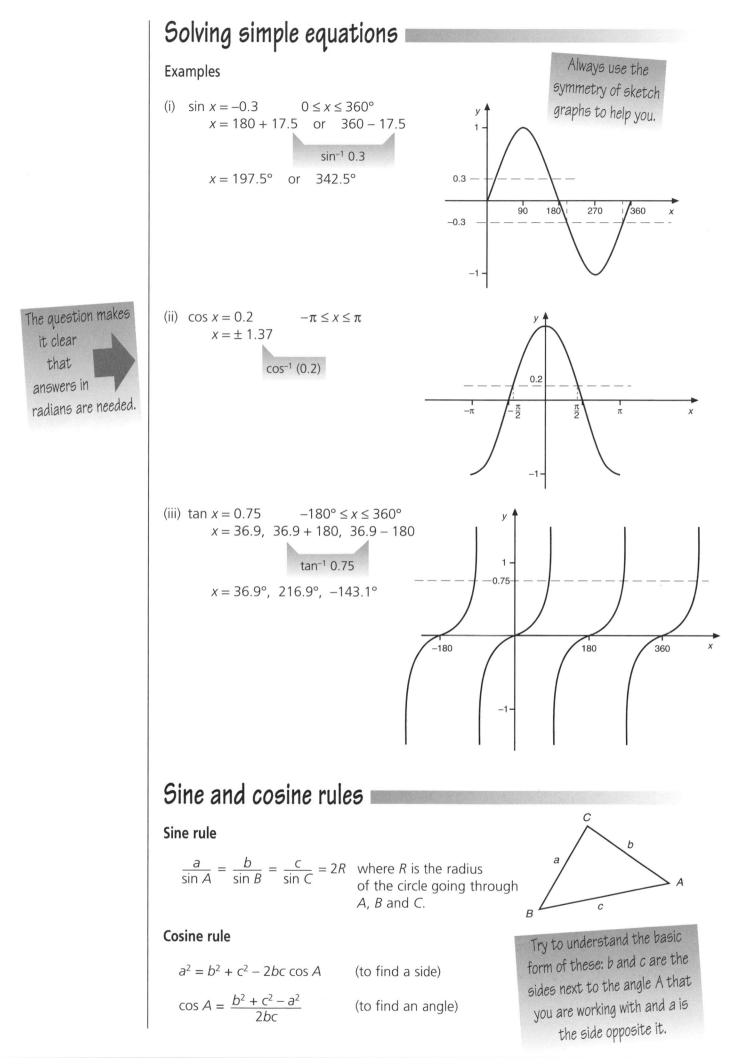

Sine and cosine rules

Sine rule

$$\frac{a}{\sin A} = \frac{b}{\sin B} = \frac{c}{\sin C} = 2R$$

where R is the radius of the circle going through A, B and C.

Cosine rule

$$a^2 = b^2 + c^2 - 2bc \cos A \qquad \text{(to find a side)}$$

$$\cos A = \frac{b^2 + c^2 - a^2}{2bc} \qquad \text{(to find an angle)}$$

Try to understand the basic form of these: b and c are the sides next to the angle A that you are working with and a is the side opposite it.

Examples

(i) Find x in each of the following triangles.

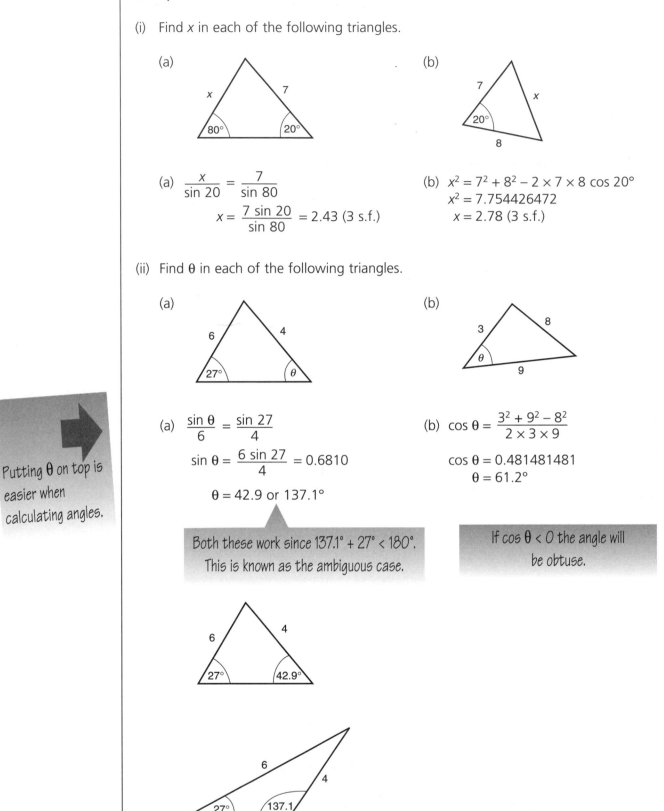

(a)

(b)

(a) $\dfrac{x}{\sin 20} = \dfrac{7}{\sin 80}$

$x = \dfrac{7 \sin 20}{\sin 80} = 2.43$ (3 s.f.)

(b) $x^2 = 7^2 + 8^2 - 2 \times 7 \times 8 \cos 20°$
$x^2 = 7.754426472$
$x = 2.78$ (3 s.f.)

(ii) Find θ in each of the following triangles.

(a)

(b)

Putting θ on top is easier when calculating angles.

(a) $\dfrac{\sin \theta}{6} = \dfrac{\sin 27}{4}$

$\sin \theta = \dfrac{6 \sin 27}{4} = 0.6810$

$\theta = 42.9$ or $137.1°$

Both these work since $137.1° + 27° < 180°$.
This is known as the ambiguous case.

(b) $\cos \theta = \dfrac{3^2 + 9^2 - 8^2}{2 \times 3 \times 9}$

$\cos \theta = 0.481481481$
$\theta = 61.2°$

If $\cos \theta < 0$ the angle will be obtuse.

Watch this one.

In problems involving bearings don't forget the fundamental principles – start by facing north, turn clockwise and **always** give three digits before the decimal point.

Graphs of secant, cosecant and cotangent

- $\sec \theta = \dfrac{1}{\cos \theta}$

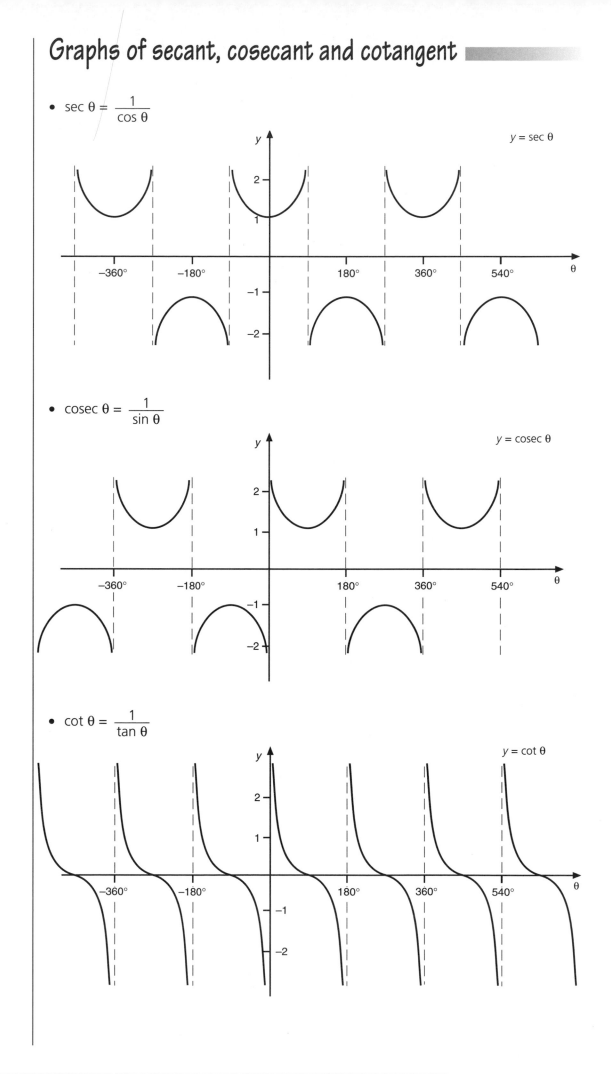

$y = \sec \theta$

- $\operatorname{cosec} \theta = \dfrac{1}{\sin \theta}$

$y = \operatorname{cosec} \theta$

- $\cot \theta = \dfrac{1}{\tan \theta}$

$y = \cot \theta$

Important trigonometric identities

These should be learnt thoroughly to help you tackle questions effectively.

Remember that $\sin^2\theta$ means $(\sin\theta)^2$.

- $\sin^2\theta + \cos^2\theta \equiv 1$

- $\sec^2\theta \equiv 1 + \tan^2\theta$

- $\text{cosec}^2\theta \equiv 1 + \cot^2\theta$

- $\tan\theta \equiv \dfrac{\sin\theta}{\cos\theta}$

- $\sin A + \sin B \equiv 2 \sin \dfrac{A+B}{2} \cos \dfrac{A-B}{2}$ (*)

- $\sin A - \sin B \equiv 2 \cos \dfrac{A+B}{2} \sin \dfrac{A-B}{2}$

- $\cos A + \cos B \equiv 2 \cos \dfrac{A+B}{2} \cos \dfrac{A-B}{2}$

- $\cos A - \cos B \equiv -2 \sin \dfrac{A+B}{2} \sin \dfrac{A-B}{2}$

- $\sin(A \pm B) \equiv \sin A \cos B \pm \cos A \sin B$

- $\cos(A \pm B) \equiv \cos A \cos B \mp \sin A \sin B$

- $\tan(A \pm B) \equiv \dfrac{\tan A \pm \tan B}{1 \mp \tan A \tan B}$

- $\sin 2A \equiv 2 \sin A \cos A$

- $\cos 2A \equiv 2 \cos^2 A - 1$
  $\equiv 1 - 2 \sin^2 A$
  $\equiv \cos^2 A - \sin^2 A$

- $\tan 2A \equiv \dfrac{2 \tan A}{1 - \tan^2 A}$

- $\sin 3A \equiv 3 \sin A - 4\sin^3 A$

- $\cos 3A = 4 \cos^3 A - 3 \cos A.$

> Try to incorporate understanding into your learning, e.g. * is 'sine plus sine is twice the sine of half the sum, cosine of half the difference'. This will help you to transfer your understanding if the symbols are not A and B.

Solving more complex trigonometric equations

It is vital that you do things in the correct order when solving more complex trigonometric equations.

Example

Find the solutions of $\sin\left(2x + \dfrac{\pi}{6}\right) = 0.5$ $0 \leq x \leq \pi$

If $0 \leq x \leq \pi$ then $0 \leq 2x \leq 2\pi$ Multiply by 2.

and $\dfrac{\pi}{6} \leq 2x + \dfrac{\pi}{6} \leq 2\pi + \dfrac{\pi}{6}$ Add $\dfrac{\pi}{6}$.

The context makes it clear that the angle is in radians.

Consider $\sin X = 0.5$ for $\dfrac{\pi}{6} \leq X \leq 2\pi + \dfrac{\pi}{6}$

$X = \dfrac{\pi}{6}$ or $2\pi - \dfrac{\pi}{6} = \dfrac{5\pi}{6}$

$2x + \dfrac{\pi}{6} = \dfrac{\pi}{6}$ or $\dfrac{5\pi}{6}$

$2x = 0$ or $\dfrac{4\pi}{6}$ Subtract $\dfrac{\pi}{6}$.

$x = 0$ or $\dfrac{\pi}{3}$ Divide by 2.

Look for opportunities to use standard trigonometric identities.

Examples

(i) Solve

$$\sin \theta = 3 \cos \theta.$$

$$\Rightarrow \quad \tan \theta = 3 \text{ etc.}$$

$\dfrac{\sin \theta}{\cos \theta} = 3$

(ii) Solve $\cos x \cos 40° + \sin x \sin 40° = 0.6$.

$$\cos(x - 40°) = 0.6 \text{ etc.}$$

(iii) Solve

$$\cos 2x + \cos x = 0.$$
$$(2\cos^2 x - 1) + \cos x = 0$$
$$2\cos^2 x + \cos x - 1 = 0$$
$$(2\cos x - 1)(\cos x + 1) = 0 \text{ etc.}$$

Expressions of the form $R \cos(\theta - \alpha)$

$R \cos(\theta - \alpha) \equiv R \cos \theta \cos \alpha + R \sin \theta \sin \alpha$.

So if $R \cos(\theta - \alpha) = a \cos \theta + b \sin \theta$
$\qquad\quad R \cos \alpha = a \quad$ and $\quad R \sin \alpha = b$

$$R = \sqrt{a^2 + b^2} \quad \text{and} \quad \tan \alpha = \frac{b}{a}$$

Example

Solve $2 \cos \theta + 3 \sin \theta = 1 \qquad 0 \le \theta \le 2\pi$

$$R = \sqrt{2^2 + 3^2} = \sqrt{13}$$

$$\tan \alpha = \frac{3}{2} \quad \Rightarrow \quad \alpha = 0.98279$$

$$\sqrt{13} \ \cos(\theta - 0.98279) = 1$$

$$\cos(\theta - 0.98279) = \frac{1}{\sqrt{13}}$$

$$\theta - 0.98279 = 1.28976 \text{ or } 2\pi - 1.28976$$

$$\theta = 2.27 \text{ or } 5.98 \ \ (3 \text{ s.f.})$$

- For an expression of the form $a \sin \theta - b \cos \theta$, the form $R \sin(\theta - \alpha)$ can be used in a similar way.

Example

Find the maximum value of $2 \sin \theta - 3 \cos \theta$ and the value of θ for which it occurs in $0 \le \theta \le 360°$.

$$R \sin(\theta - \alpha) = R \sin \theta \cos \alpha - R \cos \theta \sin \alpha$$
$$R \cos \alpha = 2 \quad \text{and} \quad R \sin \alpha = 3$$

$$R = \sqrt{2^2 + 3^2} = \sqrt{13}$$

$$\tan \alpha = \frac{R \sin \alpha}{R \cos \alpha} = \frac{3}{2} \quad \Rightarrow \quad \alpha = 56.3°$$

Maximum value is $\sqrt{13}$ when $\theta - 56.3° = 90°$
$$\text{i.e. } \theta = 146.3°$$

Proving trigonometric identities

Some general principles which will help are the following:

1 Start with the most complicated side and work towards the other side by a series of logical steps.

2 Keep an eye on the other side and use it to look for clues – these may help you to know what to do next.

3 At each stage do those things that seem sensible e.g. put fractions over a common denominator, use a relevant identity etc.

4 If things are becoming more and more complicated at each step, stop and try another approach – you are probably going about it the wrong way.

Example

Prove that $\dfrac{\cos 2A}{\cos A - \sin A} = \cos A + \sin A$

L.H.S. $= \dfrac{\cos 2A}{\cos A - \sin A}$ Left-hand side is most complicated.

$= \dfrac{\cos^2 A - \sin^2 A}{\cos A - \sin A}$ The 'hint' on the R.H.S. is that there is no '2A' term so use an appropriate identity.

$= \dfrac{(\cos A + \sin A)(\cos A - \sin A)}{(\cos A - \sin A)}$ Difference of two squares.

$= \cos A + \sin A =$ R.H.S.

Areas of triangles

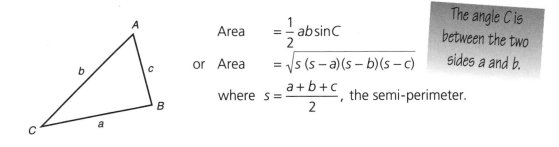

Area $= \dfrac{1}{2} ab \sin C$

or   Area $= \sqrt{s(s-a)(s-b)(s-c)}$

where $s = \dfrac{a+b+c}{2}$, the semi-perimeter.

The angle C is between the two sides a and b.

Small angle approximations

If θ is small and in radians

- $\sin \theta \approx \theta$
- $\cos \theta \approx 1 - \dfrac{1}{2}\theta^2$
- $\tan \theta \approx \theta$

Circular measure

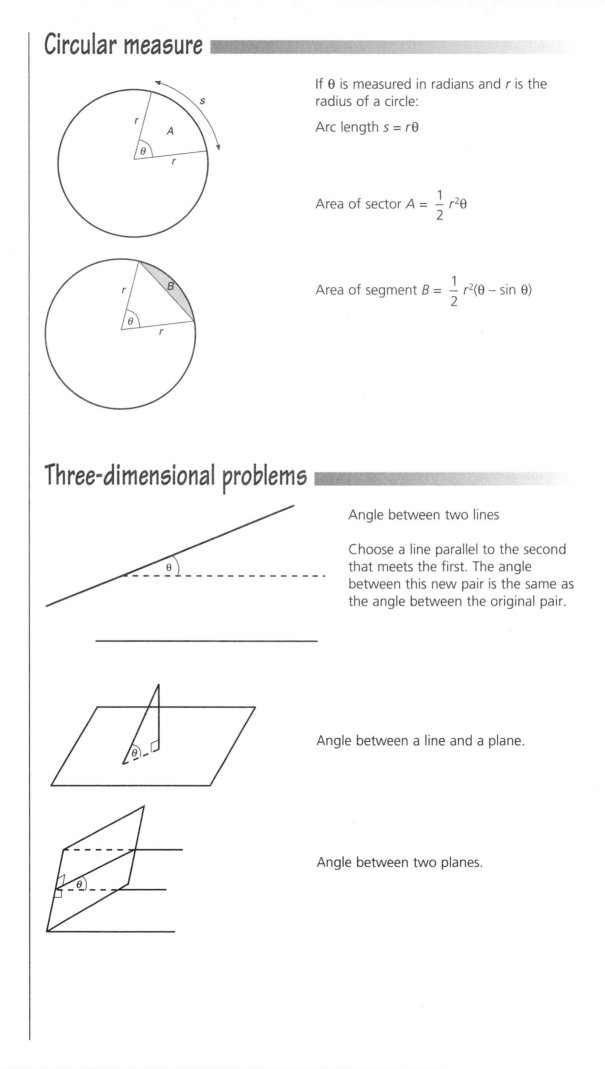

If θ is measured in radians and r is the radius of a circle:

Arc length $s = r\theta$

Area of sector $A = \dfrac{1}{2} r^2\theta$

Area of segment $B = \dfrac{1}{2} r^2(\theta - \sin\theta)$

Three-dimensional problems

Angle between two lines

Choose a line parallel to the second that meets the first. The angle between this new pair is the same as the angle between the original pair.

Angle between a line and a plane.

Angle between two planes.

Example

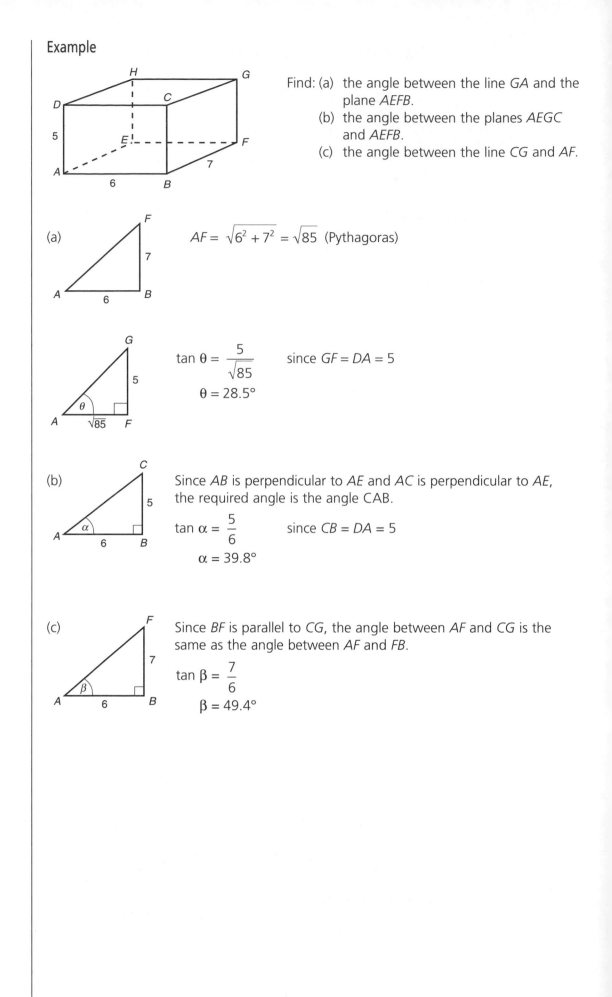

Find: (a) the angle between the line GA and the plane $AEFB$.

(b) the angle between the planes $AEGC$ and $AEFB$.

(c) the angle between the line CG and AF.

(a) $AF = \sqrt{6^2 + 7^2} = \sqrt{85}$ (Pythagoras)

$\tan \theta = \dfrac{5}{\sqrt{85}}$ since $GF = DA = 5$

$\theta = 28.5°$

(b) Since AB is perpendicular to AE and AC is perpendicular to AE, the required angle is the angle CAB.

$\tan \alpha = \dfrac{5}{6}$ since $CB = DA = 5$

$\alpha = 39.8°$

(c) Since BF is parallel to CG, the angle between AF and CG is the same as the angle between AF and FB.

$\tan \beta = \dfrac{7}{6}$

$\beta = 49.4°$

Questions

1 If $\sin \theta = \dfrac{2}{3}$ and θ is obtuse find $\cos \theta$.

2 Solve each of the following equations:

   (a) $\tan\left(\dfrac{x}{2} - 30\right) = 1$ $0 \le x \le 360°$

   (b) $\sec 3x = 3$ $0 \le x \le 2\pi$
   (c) $2 \sin \theta \cos \theta = 1$ $0 \le \theta \le \pi/2$
   (d) $\cos 2x = \sin x$ $-180° \le x \le 180°$
   (e) $2\sec^2 \theta + \tan \theta - 3 = 0$ $0 \le \theta \le 180°$

3 A ship travels 4 km on a bearing of 030° and then 5 km on a bearing of 060°. Find:

   (a) the distance of the ship from its starting point.
   (b) the bearing of the ship from its starting point.

4 Three friends are throwing a ball to each other. Alice and Bob are 10 m apart, Bernard and Claire are 20 m apart and Alice and Charles are 15 m apart. Alice walks the shortest distance possible to stand on the line joining Bob and Charles. How far does she walk?

5 Solve the equation $6 \cos t + 2 \sin t = 5$ for $-\dfrac{\pi}{2} \le t \le \dfrac{\pi}{2}$.

6 Solve the equation $4 \sin x - 7 \cos x = 0.9$ for $0 \le x \le 180°$.

7 Prove the following trigonometric identities:

   (a) $\cos^2 A + \cos 2A \equiv 2 - 3 \sin^2 A$
   (b) $\cot 2A \equiv \operatorname{cosec} 2A - \tan A$
   (c) $\tan (45 + A)° \tan (45 - A)° \equiv 1$
   (d) $\dfrac{\sin \theta}{1 - \cos \theta} + \dfrac{\sin \theta}{1 + \cos \theta} \equiv 2 \operatorname{cosec} \theta$

8 Find the area of each of the following triangles:

   (a)

   (b)

9 A chord of a circle of radius 3 cm subtends an angle of 45° at the centre of the circle. Find the area of the segment formed by this chord and the minor arc.

10 A square-based pyramid has base $ABCD$ and the vertex O is directly above the centre of the base. Given that $OA = 7$ cm and $AB = 4$ cm find:

   (a) the angle between the line OA and the base;
   (b) the angle between the planes OAB and OCD;
   (c) the angle between the lines OA and CD.

Calculus 1: differentiation

Basics

- The gradient function of the curve $y = f(x)$ is represented by the symbol $\dfrac{dy}{dx}$.

- $\dfrac{dy}{dx}$ is known as the (first) derivative of y with respect to x or the (first) differential coefficient of y with respect to x.

- When $f(x)$ is differentiated the symbol $f'(x)$ is used.

- The following basic results can be quoted from memory.

$f(x)$	$f'(x)$
ax^n	nax^{n-1}
$\sin x$	$\cos x$
$\cos x$	$-\sin x$
$\tan x$	$\sec^2 x$
$\operatorname{cosec} x$	$-\operatorname{cosec} x \cot x$
$\sec x$	$\sec x \tan x$
$\cot x$	$-\operatorname{cosec}^2 x$
e^x	e^x
e^{ax}	ae^{ax}
a^x	$(\ln a)\, a^x$
$\ln x$	$\dfrac{1}{x}$
$\log_a x$	$\dfrac{1}{(\ln a)\, x}$
$\sin^{-1}\left(\dfrac{bx}{a}\right)$	$\dfrac{b}{\sqrt{a^2 - b^2 x^2}}$
$\tan^{-1}\left(\dfrac{bx}{a}\right)$	$\dfrac{ab}{\sqrt{a^2 + b^2 x^2}}$

You are strongly advised to learn these.

Notice the – sign each time there is a 'co–'.

Rules for differentiating more complex functions

Differentiating sums and differences

Differentiate each part separately and add or subtract the results as appropriate.

Example

$$\frac{d}{dx}(x^7 - \tan x + \ln x) = \frac{d}{dx}(x^7) - \frac{d}{dx}(\tan x) + \frac{d}{dx}(\ln x)$$

$$= 7x^6 - \sec^2 x + \frac{1}{x}$$

$\dfrac{d}{dx}$ *means differentiate with respect to x.*

 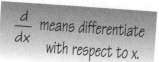

Differentiating products and quotients

Some simple products and quotients can be dealt with by using algebraic simplification first.

Examples

(i) $\dfrac{d}{dx}\left[(x+1)(2x-7)\right] = \dfrac{d}{dx}(2x^2 - 5x - 7)$

$\qquad\qquad\qquad\qquad = 4x - 5$

(ii) $\dfrac{d}{dx}\left(\dfrac{x+1}{x^2}\right) = \dfrac{d}{dx}\left(\dfrac{1}{x} + \dfrac{1}{x^2}\right)$

$\qquad\qquad\qquad = \dfrac{d}{dx}(x^{-1} + x^{-2})$

$\qquad\qquad\qquad = -x^{-2} - 2x^{-3}$

$\qquad\qquad\qquad = -\dfrac{1}{x^2} - \dfrac{2}{x^3}$

More complicated examples require the use of the product rule or the quotient rule.

- The **product rule** says if $y = uv$ where u and v are functions of x

$\dfrac{dy}{dx} = u\dfrac{dv}{dx} + v\dfrac{dy}{dx}.$

> This means the first times the derivative of the second plus the second times the derivative of the first.

Example

$\dfrac{d}{dx}(x^3 \ln x) = x^3 \dfrac{d}{dx}(\ln x) + (\ln x)\dfrac{d}{dx}(x^3)$

$\qquad\qquad\quad = x^3 \times \dfrac{1}{x} + (\ln x) \times 3x^2$

$\qquad\qquad\quad = x^2 + 3x^2 \ln x.$

- The **quotient rule** says if $y = \dfrac{u}{v}$ where again u and v are functions of x

$\dfrac{dy}{dx} = \dfrac{v\dfrac{du}{dx} - u\dfrac{dv}{dx}}{v^2}.$

> This means the bottom times the derivative of the top minus the top times the derivative of the bottom, all divided by the bottom squared.

Example

$\dfrac{d}{dx}\left(\dfrac{x^2}{\cos x}\right) = \dfrac{(\cos x)\dfrac{d}{dx}(x^2) - x^2 \dfrac{d}{dx}(\cos x)}{(\cos x)^2}$

$\qquad\qquad\qquad = \dfrac{(\cos x)\,2x - x^2(-\sin x)}{(\cos x)^2}$

$\qquad\qquad\qquad = \dfrac{2x\cos x + x^2 \sin x}{\cos^2 x}$

Chain rule

Functions of functions (composite functions) need to be differentiated using the **chain rule**.

- If $y = f(u)$ where u is a function of x

$$\frac{dy}{dx} = f'(u) \times \frac{du}{dx} \quad or \quad \frac{dy}{dx} = \frac{dy}{du} \times \frac{du}{dx}.$$

Examples

(i)   If $y = (x^3 + 1)^5$ then $u = x^3 + 1$

      i.e. $y = u^5$

$$\frac{dy}{du} = 5u^4 \quad and \quad \frac{du}{dx} = 3x^2$$

$$\frac{dy}{dx} = 5u^4 \times 3x^2$$

$$= 5(x^3 + 1)^4 \times 3x^2$$

$$= 15x^2 (x^3 + 1)^4$$

(ii)   If $y = \tan(e^{3x})$ then $u = e^{3x}$

      i.e. $y = \tan u$

$$\frac{dy}{du} = \sec^2 u \quad \frac{du}{dx} = 3e^{3x}$$

$$\frac{dy}{dx} = \sec^2 u \times 3e^{3x}$$

$$= 3e^{3x} \sec^2(e^{3x})$$

Differentiating inverse functions

If we know x in terms of y we can find $\dfrac{dy}{dx}$ by using the result $\dfrac{dy}{dx} = 1 \Big/ \dfrac{dx}{dy}$.

Example

If $x = \sin y$ then $\dfrac{dx}{dy} = \cos y$

$$\frac{dy}{dx} = 1 \Big/ \frac{dx}{dy}$$

$$= \frac{1}{\cos y}$$

$$= \frac{1}{\sqrt{1 - \sin^2 y}}$$

$$= \frac{1}{\sqrt{1 - x^2}}$$

It is usual to put the answer in terms of x if possible.

Differentiating functions defined implicitly

Use the rules already listed to deal with functions defined implicitly.

Examples

(i) If
$$e^y + 4xy = \cos x$$

$$e^y \frac{dy}{dx} + 4x\frac{dy}{dx} + 4y = -\sin x$$

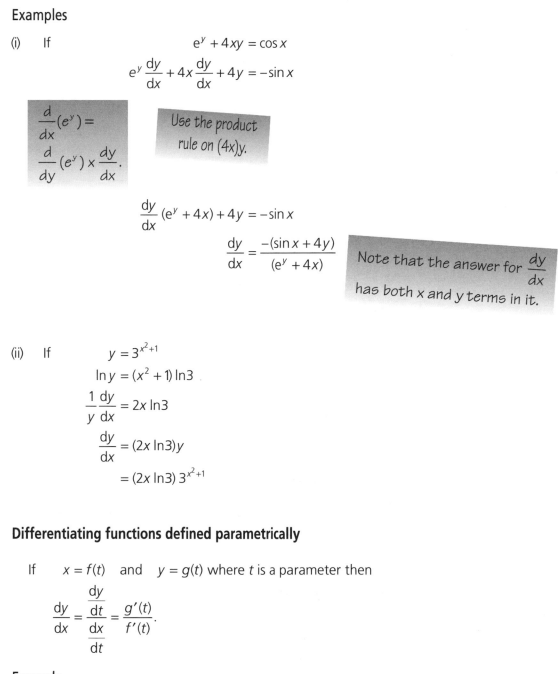

$$\frac{d}{dx}(e^y) =$$
$$\frac{d}{dy}(e^y) \times \frac{dy}{dx}.$$

Use the product rule on $(4x)y$.

$$\frac{dy}{dx}(e^y + 4x) + 4y = -\sin x$$

$$\frac{dy}{dx} = \frac{-(\sin x + 4y)}{(e^y + 4x)}$$

Note that the answer for $\frac{dy}{dx}$ has both x and y terms in it.

(ii) If
$$y = 3^{x^2+1}$$
$$\ln y = (x^2 + 1)\ln 3$$
$$\frac{1}{y}\frac{dy}{dx} = 2x \ln 3$$
$$\frac{dy}{dx} = (2x \ln 3)y$$
$$= (2x \ln 3)\, 3^{x^2+1}$$

Differentiating functions defined parametrically

If $x = f(t)$ and $y = g(t)$ where t is a parameter then

$$\frac{dy}{dx} = \frac{\dfrac{dy}{dt}}{\dfrac{dx}{dt}} = \frac{g'(t)}{f'(t)}.$$

Example

If $x = t + \sin t$ and $y = \sin 2t$

$$\frac{dx}{dt} = 1 + \cos t \qquad \frac{dy}{dt} = 2\cos 2t$$

$$\frac{dy}{dx} = \frac{2\cos 2t}{1 + \cos t}$$

Related rates of change

The chain rule can be used to solve problems dealing with related rates of change.

Example

The volume of a spherical balloon is increasing at the rate of 20 cm³/s. Find the rate at which the radius is increasing when the radius is 3 cm.

$$V = \frac{4}{3}\pi r^3 \quad \text{so} \quad \frac{dV}{dr} = 4\pi r^2$$

We know that $\dfrac{dV}{dt} = \dfrac{dV}{dr} \times \dfrac{dr}{dt}$ by the chain rule,

$$\text{so} \quad \frac{dr}{dt} = \frac{\dfrac{dV}{dt}}{\dfrac{dV}{dr}} = \frac{20\pi}{4\pi \times 3^2} = \frac{5}{9} \text{ cm/s.}$$

Second derivative

The second derivative of y with respect to x, $\dfrac{d^2y}{dx^2}$, is useful in certain circumstances.

It is obtained by differentiating $\dfrac{dy}{dx}$ with respect to x.

It is therefore the gradient of the gradient function.

Stationary points

A stationary point is one where $\dfrac{dy}{dx} = 0$.

There are three types of stationary point:

- a (local) maximum point
- a (local) minimum point
- a point of inflexion.

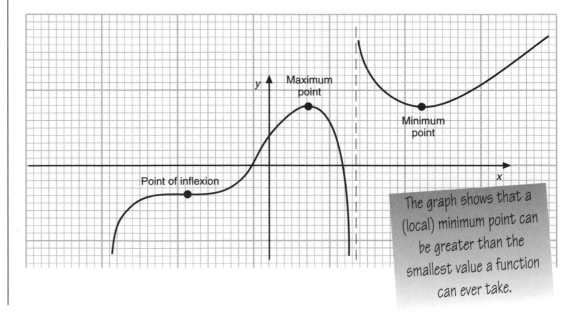

The graph shows that a (local) minimum point can be greater than the smallest value a function can ever take.

Having found where $\dfrac{dy}{dx} = 0$, there are two main ways of determining the nature of a stationary point, P.

1 Use of $\dfrac{dy}{dx}$ alone.

At P	Just to the left of P	Just to the right of P	Conclusion	Graph looks like
$\dfrac{dy}{dx} = 0$	$\dfrac{dy}{dx} > 0$	$\dfrac{dy}{dx} < 0$	maximum point	
$\dfrac{dy}{dx} = 0$	$\dfrac{dy}{dx} < 0$	$\dfrac{dy}{dx} > 0$	minimum point	
$\dfrac{dy}{dx} = 0$	$\dfrac{dy}{dx} < 0$	$\dfrac{dy}{dx} < 0$	point of inflexion	
$\dfrac{dy}{dx} = 0$	$\dfrac{dy}{dx} > 0$	$\dfrac{dy}{dx} > 0$	point of inflexion	

2 Use of $\dfrac{d^2y}{dx^2}$.

$\dfrac{dy}{dx}$	$\dfrac{d^2y}{dx^2}$	Conclusion
0	< 0	maximum point
0	> 0	minimum point
0	$= 0$ and changes sign on either side of P	point of inflexion

It is possible to have points of inflexion which are not stationary. The condition for this is that $\dfrac{dy}{dx} \neq 0$ and $\dfrac{d^2y}{dx^2} = 0$.

Example

Find the coordinates of the stationary point on the curve $y = xe^{-x}$ and determine its nature.

$$\frac{dy}{dx} = -xe^{-x} + e^{-x} = e^{-x}(1 - x)$$

$$\frac{dy}{dx} = 0 \quad when \quad x = 1 \quad since \quad e^{-x} \neq 0 \quad \text{for all values of } x.$$

Then either by method 1

$$\left.\frac{dy}{dx}\right|_{x=0.9} = e^{-0.9} \times (1 - 0.9) = 0.04 > 0$$

$$\left.\frac{dy}{dx}\right|_{x=1.1} = e^{-1.1}(1 - 1.1) = -0.03 < 0$$

giving a maximum point at $(1, e^{-1})$,

or by method 2

$$\frac{d^2y}{dx^2} = e^{-x}(-1) - e^{-x}(1-x)$$

$$= e^{-x}(x-2)$$

Use the product rule on $e^{-x}(1-x)$.

$$\left.\frac{d^2y}{dx^2}\right|_{x=1} = e^{-1}(1-2) = -0.4 < 0$$

giving a maximum point at $(1, e^{-1})$.

The value of y is called a stationary value (or in this particular case a maximum value).

Practical maximum and minimum problems

In this type of problem practical use is made of finding a maximum and/or minimum value in a 'real-life' problem.

Example

A cylindrical tin has a volume of 128π cm³. Find the dimensions for the tin in order to have the minimum possible surface area, and find the minimum possible surface area.

Surface area, $\quad S = 2\pi r^2 + 2\pi r h$

Circular ends.   Curved surface.

$$V = \pi r^2 h = 128\pi$$

$$h = \frac{128}{r^2}$$

Volume of a cylinder is $\pi r^2 h$ and we know the volume to be 128π.

h

r

The trick is to eliminate one of the variables

$$S = 2\pi r^2 + 2\pi r \frac{128}{r^2}$$

$$= 2\pi r^2 + \frac{256\pi}{r}$$

$$\frac{dS}{dr} = 4\pi r - \frac{256\pi}{r^2}; \qquad \frac{d^2S}{dr^2} = 4\pi + \frac{512\pi}{r^3}$$

$$\frac{dS}{dr} = 0 \quad when \quad 4\pi r - \frac{256\pi}{r^2} = 0 \Rightarrow r^3 = 64 \Rightarrow r = 4 \text{ cm}$$

$$\left.\frac{d^2S}{dr^2}\right|_{r=4} = 4\pi + 8\pi = 12\pi > 0 \quad \text{i.e. } S \text{ is a minimum value.}$$

$$h = \frac{128}{4^2} = 8 \text{ cm}$$

So the height is 8 cm and the radius is 4 cm.

$$S_{min} = 2\pi \times 4^2 + \frac{256\pi}{4} = 96\pi \text{ cm}^2.$$

Finding the equation of a tangent at a point

Steps: 1 Find $\dfrac{dy}{dx}$ and evaluate it at the given point.

2 Write down and simplify the equation of the straight line going through the required point with the calculated gradient.

Finding the equation of a normal at a point

Steps: 1 Find $\dfrac{dy}{dx}$ and evaluate it at the given point.

2 Find the gradient of the normal using the fact that gradient of normal
$$= \frac{-1}{\text{gradient of tangent}}.$$

3 Write down and simplify an equation of the straight line going through the required point with the calculated gradient.

Example

Find the equations of the tangent and normal to the curve $y = x^3 + 2$ at $x = 1$.

When $x = 1$, $y = 1^3 + 2 = 3$

$$\frac{dy}{dx} = 3x^2 \Rightarrow \left.\frac{dy}{dx}\right|_{x=1} = 3, \quad \text{which is the gradient of the tangent.}$$

Equation of tangent is

$$\frac{y-3}{x-1} = 3$$

$$y - 3 = 3(x - 1)$$

$$y = 3x.$$

Gradient of normal $= -\dfrac{1}{3}$.

Equation of normal is

$$\frac{y-3}{x-1} = -\frac{1}{3}$$

$$3(y - 3) = -(x - 1)$$

$$3y = -x + 10.$$

Questions

1 Differentiate each of the following, simplifying your answers:

   (a) $\tan 3x$

   (b) $\sec x \tan x$

   (c) $x^3 \sin x$

   (d) $\dfrac{e^x}{x^2}$

   (e) $\sqrt{x^2 + 1}$

   (f) $\cot (\ln x)$

   (g) 2^x

   (h) $\sin^{-1} \left(\dfrac{3x}{2} \right)$

2 Find $\dfrac{dy}{dx}$ in each of the following cases:

   (a) $y^3 + 3xy = e^x \sin y$
   (b) $x = 3e^t + \cos t, \ y = \sin t - e^{-t}$
   (c) $e^y = x^2 + x$
   (d) $x = y^n$
   (e) $x = \tan y$

3 The radius of a circle, r, increases at a rate of 0.5 cm/s. Find, in terms of r, an expression for the rate at which the area of the circle is increasing.

4 Find, and determine the nature of, the stationary points on the curves:

   (a) $y = 5x^6 - 12x^5$
   (b) $y = x\ln x$

5 A solid cylinder of height h and radius r has surface area 600 cm². Find the dimensions for which the volume is a maximum and find this maximum value.

6 A cuboid has a square base of length x cm. The total surface area is 600 cm².

   (a) Show that the volume of the block is $x - x^3$ cm³.
   (b) Find the length of the base for which the volume is a maximum.
   (c) Find the maximum volume.

7 Find the equations of the tangent and normal to the curve $y = x(x + 1)$ when $x = 2$.

8 A curve is given paramerically by $x = t^2, \ y = t^3$.

   (a) Show that an equation of the tangent to the curve at the point (4, 8) is
        $y = 3x - 4$.

   The tangent meets the curve again at the point Q.

   (b) Find the coordinates of Q.

Calculus 2: integration

- Integration is the opposite of differentiation.

- If $\dfrac{d}{dx}\left[f(x)\right] = f'(x)$ then $\int f'(x)\,dx = f(x) + c$

  where c is an arbitrary constant of integration.

Integrals of standard functions

The following results are best memorised.

$f(x)$	$\int f(x)\,dx$
ax^n	$\dfrac{ax^{n+1}}{n+1} + c$
e^x	e^x
e^{ax}	$\dfrac{1}{a}e^{ax}$
a^x	$\dfrac{a^x}{\ln a} + c$
$\dfrac{1}{x}$	$\ln|x| + c$
$\sin x$	$-\cos x + c$
$\cos x$	$\sin x + c$
$\tan x$	$\ln|\sec x| + c$
$\operatorname{cosec} x$	$-\ln|\operatorname{cosec} x + \cot x| + c$
$\sec x$	$\ln|\sec x + \tan x| + c$
$\cot x$	$\ln|\sin x| + c$
$\sec^2 x$	$\tan x + c$
$\operatorname{cosec}^2 x$	$-\cot x + c$
$\sec x \tan x$	$\sec x + c$
$\operatorname{cosec} x \cot x$	$-\operatorname{cosec} x + c$
$\dfrac{b}{\sqrt{a^2 - b^2 x^2}}$	$\sin^{-1}\left(\dfrac{bx}{a}\right) + c$
$\dfrac{ab}{a^2 + b^2 x^2}$	$\tan^{-1}\left(\dfrac{bx}{a}\right) + c$

Integration techniques

Integration of sums and differences

$$\int \left[f(x) \pm g(x) \right] dx = \int f(x)\, dx \pm \int g(x)\, dx$$

Example

$$\int (\cos x + x^3)\, dx = \int \cos x\, dx + \int x^3 dx$$

$$= \sin x + \frac{x^4}{4} + c$$

Use of simple algebraic techniques

Examples

(i)
$$\int \frac{(x^2 + 1)^2}{x^3}\, dx = \int \frac{(x^4 + 2x^2 + 1)}{x^3}\, dx$$

$$= \int \left(x + \frac{2}{x} + \frac{1}{x^3} \right) dx$$

$$= \frac{x^2}{2} + 2\ln|x| - \frac{1}{2x^2} + c$$

> Since $\int \dfrac{1}{x^3}\, dx = \int x^{-3} dx = \dfrac{x^{-2}}{2}$.

(ii)
$$\int \frac{x}{x-1}\, dx = \int \left(\frac{x-1+1}{x-1} \right) dx$$

$$= \int \left(1 + \frac{1}{x-1} \right) dx$$

$$= x + \ln|x-1| + c$$

Reverse differentiation

- $\displaystyle \int f'(x) [f(x)]^n\, dx \quad = \frac{[f(x)]^{n+1}}{n+1} + c$

- $\displaystyle \int f'(x)\, e^{f(x)}\, dx \quad = e^{f(x)} + c$

- $\displaystyle \int \frac{f'(x)}{f(x)}\, dx \quad = \ln|f(x)| + c$

- $\displaystyle \int f'(x)\, g'[f(x)]\, dx = g[f(x)] + c$

- The key issue is to check by differentiating and modify any constants as necessary.

Examples

(i) $\displaystyle \int 2x\,(x^2+1)^7 dx = \frac{(x^2+1)^8}{8} + c$

> Differentiating $(x^2+1)^8$ gives $8\,(x^2+1)^7\,(2x)$ by the chain rule. We have 8 times too much so divide by 8.

(ii) $\int \dfrac{\cos\theta}{2\sin\theta + 1}\, d\theta = \dfrac{1}{2}\ln|2\sin\theta + 1| + c$

> Differentiating $\ln|2\sin\theta + 1|$ gives $\dfrac{2\cos\theta}{2\sin\theta + 1}$ which is 2 times too much so divide by 2.

(iii) $\int \sec^2(3\theta)\, d\theta = \dfrac{1}{3}\tan(3\theta) + c$

> Differentiating $\tan 3\theta$ gives $(\sec^2 3\theta) \times 3$ so divide by 3.

(iv) $\int \sqrt{2x + 1}\, dx = \dfrac{1}{3}(2x + 1)^{3/2} + c$

> Differentiating $(2x + 1)^{3/2}$ gives $\dfrac{3}{2}(2x + 1)^{1/2} \times (2x)$ which is 3 times too much so divide by 3.

Long division and partial fractions

Long division and partial fractions can be used to integrate functions of the form $\dfrac{f(x)}{g(x)}$ where $f(x)$ and $g(x)$ are polynomials.

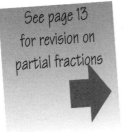
See page 13 for revision on partial fractions

Example

$$\int \frac{7x^2 - 20x + 7}{(2x + 1)(x - 2)^2}\, dx$$

$$= \int \left[\frac{3}{2x + 1} + \frac{2}{x - 2} - \frac{1}{(x - 2)^2} \right] dx$$

$$= \frac{3}{2}\ln|2x + 1| + 2\ln|x - 2| + \frac{1}{x - 2} + c$$

Integrands of the form $\sin^m x \cos^n x$, where n or m are odd

Example

$$\int \sin^3 x \cos^2 x\, dx = \int \sin x\,(1 - \cos^2 x)\cos^2 x\, dx$$

$$= \int (\cos^2 x \sin x - \cos^4 x \sin x)\, dx$$

$$= -\frac{\cos^3 x}{3} + \frac{\cos^5 x}{5} + c$$

> Extract the 'odd' power as a factor and use $\sin^2 x + \cos^2 x = 1$.

Integrands of the form $\sin^m x \cos^n x$, where n and m are even

Example

$$\int \sin^2 x \cos^2 x\, dx = \int \left(\frac{1}{2} - \frac{1}{2}\cos 2x \right)\left(\frac{1}{2} + \frac{1}{2}\cos 2x \right) dx$$

$$= \int \left(\frac{1}{4} - \frac{1}{4}\cos^2 2x \right) dx = \int \left(\frac{1}{4} - \frac{1}{4}\left(\frac{1}{2} + \frac{1}{2}\cos 4x \right) \right) dx$$

$$= \int \left(\frac{1}{8} - \frac{1}{8}\cos 4x \right) dx = \frac{x}{8} - \frac{1}{32}\sin 4x + c$$

> Use rearrangements of the double angle formula $\cos 2A = 2\cos^2 A - 1$ $= 1 - 2\sin^2 A$.

Use of suitable identities

Examples

(i) $\qquad \int \tan^2 x \, dx = \int (\sec^2 x - 1) \, dx = \tan x - x + c$

(ii) $\qquad \int \cot x \, dx = \int \dfrac{\cos x}{\sin x} \, dx = \ln |\sin x| + c$

> The numerator is the derivative of the denominator.

(iii) $\int \cos 7x \cos 3x \, dx = \int \dfrac{1}{2} (\cos 10x + \cos 4x) \, dx$

$$= \dfrac{1}{20} \sin 10x + \dfrac{1}{8} \sin 4x + c$$

This uses one of the rearrangements of the identities on page 58 of the type:

$$\cos P \cos Q = \dfrac{1}{2} \left[\cos (P + Q) + \cos (P - Q) \right]$$

$$\sin P \sin Q = -\dfrac{1}{2} \left[\cos (P + Q) - \cos (P - Q) \right]$$

$$\sin P \cos Q = \dfrac{1}{2} \left[\sin (P + Q) + \sin (P - Q) \right]$$

Integration by parts

This is usually applied to products of two terms or one term where 1 can be used as another term. The aim is to simplify the integral.

$$\int u \dfrac{dv}{dx} \, dx = uv - \int v \dfrac{du}{dx} \, dx$$

Examples

(i) $\quad \int x \cos x \, dx \qquad = x \sin x - \int 1 \cdot \sin x \, dx$

$\qquad\qquad\qquad\qquad = x \sin x + \cos x + c$

(ii) $\quad \int \ln x \, dx = \int 1 \cdot \ln x \, dx = x \ln x - \int \left(x \cdot \dfrac{1}{x} \right) dx$

$\qquad\qquad\qquad = x \ln x - \int 1 \, dx$

$\qquad\qquad\qquad = x \ln x - x + c$

> **Clear, methodical layout is essential in this type of problem.**

(iii) $\quad I = \int e^x \sin x \, dx \quad = (-e^x \cos x) - \int -e^x \cos x \, dx$

> Integrating sin x gives −cos x.

> e^x differentiated is e^x.

> We appear to be no further forward. Use parts a second time the same way round.

$$I = -e^x \cos x + \int e^x \cos x \, dx$$

$$= -e^x \cos x + \left\{ e^x \sin x - \int e^x \sin x \, dx \right\}$$

> Integrating cos x gives sin x.

$$I = -e^x \cos x + e^x \sin x - \int e^x \sin x \, dx$$

$$I = -e^x \cos x + e^x \sin x - I$$

$$2I = -e^x \cos x + e^x \sin x$$

$$I = \dfrac{-e^x \cos x + e^x \sin x}{2} + c$$

> Don't forget the c.

Integration by substitution

This is a technique for simplifying the integral.

$$\int f(g(x))\,dx = \int f(u)\,\frac{dx}{du}\,du, \quad \text{where} \quad u = g(x).$$

Example

$$I = \int \sqrt{1-x^2}\,dx$$

> Put $x = \sin u$, so $\dfrac{dx}{du} = \cos u$.

$\dfrac{dx}{du}$.

$$I = \int \sqrt{1-\sin^2 u}\,\cos u\,du$$

> The reason for using $x = \sin u$ is that $1 - \sin^2 u = \cos^2 u$.

$$I = \int \sqrt{\cos^2 u}\,\cos u\,du$$

$$I = \int \cos^2 u\,du = \int \left(\frac{1}{2} + \frac{1}{2}\cos 2u\right)du$$

$$= \frac{u}{2} + \frac{\sin 2u}{4} + c$$

$$= \frac{\sin^{-1} x}{2} + \frac{\sin(2\sin^{-1} x)}{4} + c$$

> $x = \sin u$ means that $u = \sin^{-1} x$ and the original problem was in terms of x.

> The final answer should be in terms of the original variable.

Definite integrals

If $\quad F(x) = \int f(x)\,dx \quad$ then $\quad \displaystyle\int_a^b f(x)\,dx = F(b) - F(a)$.

Examples

(i)
$$\int_{\pi/4}^{\pi/2} (\cos x - x)\,dx = \left[\sin x - \frac{x^2}{2}\right]_{\pi/4}^{\pi/2}$$

$$= \left(1 - \frac{\pi^2}{8}\right) - \left(\frac{1}{\sqrt{2}} - \frac{\pi^2}{32}\right)$$

> $F(\pi/2)$. $F(\pi/4)$.

$$= 1 - \frac{1}{\sqrt{2}} - \frac{3\pi^2}{32}$$

(ii)
$$\int_0^\pi x\sin x\,dx = \left[-x\cos x\right]_0^\pi - \int_0^\pi -1\cos x\,dx$$

> $\int \sin x\,dx = -\cos x$.

$$= (\pi - 0) + \int_0^\pi \cos x\,dx$$

$$= \pi + \left[\sin x\right]_0^\pi$$

$$= \pi + (0 - 0) = \pi$$

(iii)

$$\int_1^3 \frac{1}{(1+x)\sqrt{x}}\, dx = \int_{\pi/4}^{\pi/3} \frac{1}{(1+\tan^2\theta)\sqrt{\tan^2\theta}}\, 2\tan\theta\sec^2\theta\, d\theta$$

> $\dfrac{dx}{d\theta} = 2\tan\theta\sec^2\theta.$

> Use the substitution $x = \tan^2\theta$.

If $x = 1$ $\tan^2\theta = 1$
$\Rightarrow \tan\theta = 1 \quad \Rightarrow \theta = \pi/4$
If $x = 3$ $\tan^2\theta = 3$
$\Rightarrow \tan\theta = \sqrt{3} \Rightarrow \theta = \pi/3.$

The x limits become u limits.

$$= \int_{\pi/4}^{\pi/3} \frac{1}{\sec^2\theta\,\tan\theta}\, 2\tan\theta\sec^2\theta\, d\theta$$

$$= \int_{\pi/4}^{\pi/3} 2\, d\theta$$

> $1 + \tan^2\theta = \sec^2\theta.$

$$= \Big[2\theta\Big]_{\pi/4}^{\pi/3}$$

$$= \frac{2\pi}{3} - \frac{2\pi}{4}$$

$$= \frac{2\pi}{12}$$

$$= \frac{\pi}{6}$$

Solving first-order differential equations with variables separable

Examples

(i) Find the solution of $\dfrac{dy}{dx} = y^3\cos x$ given that $y = 1$ when $x = \pi/2$.

> Rearrange to get all the x terms on one side (with dx on top line) and all y terms on the other side (with dy on top line).

$$\int \frac{dy}{y^3} = \int \cos x\, dx$$

$$\frac{-1}{2y^2} = \sin x + c$$

$$\frac{-1}{2} = 1 + c \qquad \text{Put } y = 1 \text{ and } x = \pi/2$$

$$c = \frac{-3}{2}$$

$$\frac{-1}{2y^2} = \sin x - \frac{3}{2} \Rightarrow \frac{-1}{2y^2} = \frac{2\sin x - 3}{2}$$

$$y^2 = \frac{-1}{2\sin x - 3}$$

$$= \frac{1}{3 - 2\sin x}$$

(ii) Find the general solution of $\dfrac{dy}{dx} + \dfrac{4\sec^2 x}{y} = 0$.

$$\frac{dy}{dx} = \frac{-4\sec^2 x}{y}$$

$$\int y \, dy = \int -4\sec^2 x \, dx$$

$$\frac{y^2}{2} = -4\tan x + c$$

The solution doesn't need to be in the form $y = \ldots$ unless asked for.

(iii) The rate of increase of a population P million at time t years is proportional to the population at that time. Given that at time $t = 0$, $P = 31.4$ and that at time $t = 9$, $P = 40.3$, find an expression for the size of the population in terms of t.

$$\frac{dP}{dt} = kP$$

$$\int \frac{dP}{P} = \int k \, dt$$

$$\ln P = kt + \ln c$$

Using $\ln c$ instead of c simplifies later work.

$$\ln P - \ln c = kt$$

Using laws of logarithms.

$$\ln\left(\frac{P}{c}\right) = kt$$

$$\frac{P}{c} = e^{kt}$$

$$P = c\,e^{kt}$$

At $t = 0, P = 31.4$ $\qquad 31.4 = c\,e^0 = c, \quad$ since $e^0 = 1$

$$P = 31.4\,e^{kt}$$

At $t = 9, P = 40.3$ $\qquad 9k = \ln\left(\dfrac{40.3}{31.4}\right) \quad$ since $kt = \ln\left(\dfrac{P}{c}\right)$ from above

$$k = \frac{1}{9}\ln\left(\frac{40.3}{31.4}\right)$$

$$= 0.0277 \,(3\text{ s.f.})$$

$$P = 31.4\,e^{0.0277t}$$

Areas under curves

- The area between a curve, the x-axis and the lines $x = a$ and $x = b$ is given by $\int_a^b y \, dx$.

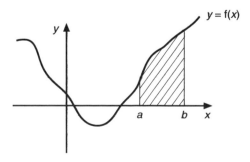

- Remember that areas below the x-axis are negative and that a quick sketch can save you from making errors.

- The area between a curve, the y-axis and the lines $y = c$ and $y = d$ is given by $\int_c^d x \, dy$.

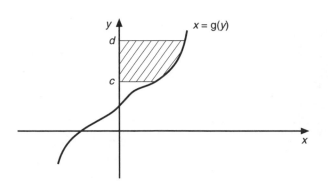

- Remember that areas to the left of the y-axis are negative and that a quick sketch can save you from making errors.

- Using simple geometric properties for areas of triangles, trapezia etc. can save you time.

Examples

(i) Find the area between the curve $y = x^2 - 7$, the x-axis and the lines $x = 2$ and $x = 3$.

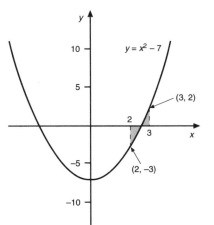

The curve meets the x-axis at $x = \sqrt{7}$.

Just doing $\int_2^3 (x^2 - 7) \, dx$ would give the wrong answer because part of the curve is below the x-axis.

The area required $= \left| \int_2^{\sqrt{7}} (x^2 - 7) \, dx \right| + \int_{\sqrt{7}}^3 (x^2 - 7) \, dx$

$$= \left| \left[\frac{x^3}{3} - 7x \right]_2^{\sqrt{7}} \right| + \left[\frac{x^3}{3} - 7x \right]_{\sqrt{7}}^3$$

$$= \left| \left(\frac{7\sqrt{7}}{3} - 7\sqrt{7} \right) - \left(\frac{8}{3} - 14 \right) \right| + (9 - 21) - \left(\frac{7\sqrt{7}}{3} - 7\sqrt{7} \right)$$

$$= \left(\frac{14}{3}\sqrt{7} - \frac{34}{3} \right) + \left(\frac{14}{3}\sqrt{7} - 12 \right)$$

$$= \frac{28}{3}\sqrt{7} - \frac{70}{3}$$

$$= 1.36 \text{ (3 s.f.)}$$

(ii) Find the area between the curve $y = x^2$, the y-axis and the lines $y = 0$ and $y = 4$ in the quadrant $x > 0$, $y > 0$.

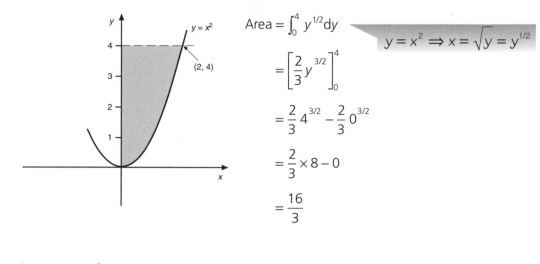

Area $= \int_0^4 y^{1/2} dy$

$y = x^2 \Rightarrow x = \sqrt{y} = y^{1/2}$

$$= \left[\frac{2}{3} y^{3/2}\right]_0^4$$

$$= \frac{2}{3} 4^{3/2} - \frac{2}{3} 0^{3/2}$$

$$= \frac{2}{3} \times 8 - 0$$

$$= \frac{16}{3}$$

Volumes of revolution

- The volume generated when the region between a curve, the x-axis and the lines $x = a$ and $x = b$ is rotated through 2π radians about the x-axis is $\int_a^b \pi y^2 \, dx$.

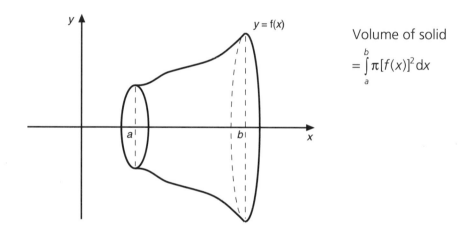

Volume of solid

$$= \int_a^b \pi[f(x)]^2 dx$$

- The volume generated when the region between a curve, the y-axis and the lines $y = c$ and $y = d$ is rotated through 2π radians about the y-axis is $\int_c^d \pi x^2 \, dy$.

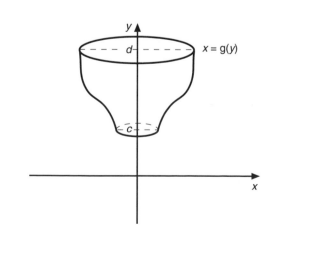

Volume of solid

$$= \int_c^d \pi[g(y)]^2 dy$$

Example

Find the volume generated when the region bounded by the curve $y = e^x$, the x-axis and the lines $x = 2$ and $x = 3$ is rotated through 2π radians about the x-axis.

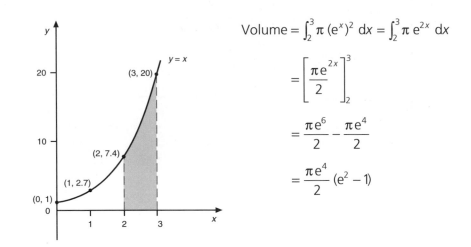

$$\text{Volume} = \int_2^3 \pi \, (e^x)^2 \, dx = \int_2^3 \pi \, e^{2x} \, dx$$

$$= \left[\frac{\pi e^{2x}}{2} \right]_2^3$$

$$= \frac{\pi e^6}{2} - \frac{\pi e^4}{2}$$

$$= \frac{\pi e^4}{2} \, (e^2 - 1)$$

Questions

1 Find each of the following integrals:

(a) $\displaystyle\int \frac{e^{2x}}{e^{2x}+3}\, dx$

(b) $\displaystyle\int 2\sec^2 x\tan^6 x\, dx$

(c) $\displaystyle\int_0^{\pi/3} \cos^2 x\, dx$

(d) $\displaystyle\int \tan^3 x\, dx$

(e) $\displaystyle\int \sin 4x\cos 2x\, dx$

(f) $\displaystyle\int \frac{2}{4+9x^2}\, dx$

(g) $\displaystyle\int \frac{2x-3}{(x-1)^2}\, dx$

(h) $\displaystyle\int_1^2 \frac{5-x}{(x+1)(2x-1)}\, dx$

(i) $\displaystyle\int_0^1 x^2\, e^x\, dx$

(j) $\displaystyle\int_1^{\sqrt{2}} \frac{1}{x^2\sqrt{4-x^2}}\, dx$

(k) $\displaystyle\int_0^{\sqrt{3}} \tan^{-1} x\, dx$

(l) $\displaystyle\int x\sqrt{1+x^2}\, dx$

(m) $\displaystyle\int x^n \ln x\, dx$

(n) $\displaystyle\int_0^{\pi/2} \sin^4 x\cos^3 x\, dx$

2 Find the solution of each of the following differential equations:

(a) $(1+x^2)\dfrac{dy}{dx}=x\,(4+y^2)$ given that $y=0$ when $x=0$.

(b) $\dfrac{dy}{dx}=\dfrac{(x+3)\sqrt{y}}{x}$

(c) $\dfrac{dy}{dx}-\dfrac{\sec 2y}{x^2+x-2}=0$

(d) $x\dfrac{dy}{dx}=\cos^2 y$ given that $x>0$ and that $y=\pi/3$ when $x=1$.

3 The diagram shows the curve $y = -x^2 - 2x + 3$ and the line $y = -2x$. Find the shaded area.

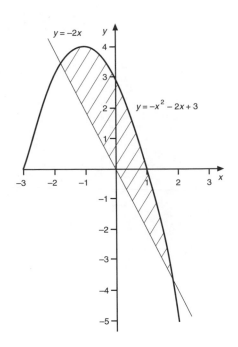

4 The region between the curve $y = \dfrac{x^2 + 1}{x}$, the lines $x = 1$ and $x = 2$ and the x-axis is rotated through π radians about the x-axis. Find the volume generated.

5 The speed of a chemical reaction is given by the differential equation

$$\frac{dx}{dt} = k\,(a - x)$$

where k and a are constants, and x kg is the amount of substance transformed at time t. At time $t = 0$, $x = 0$. Find an expression for x in terms of t.

Numerical methods

Errors

- The (maximum) absolute error is the magnitude of the difference between the true value and the observed value.

Example

If a measurement is 7 km to the nearest kilometre then the true value, x km, is given by $6.5 \leq x < 7.5$. The absolute error is 0.5 km.

- The relative error $= \dfrac{\text{absolute error}}{\text{true value}}$.

As the true value is often not known, the observed value is often used to estimate it. In the above example

$$\text{relative error} = \frac{0.5}{7} = 0.0714 \ (3 \text{ s.f.})$$

- The percentage relative error = relative error × 100.

  In our example this was 7.14%.

- When combining two results:

  * absolute error in $a \pm b$ = absolute error in a + absolute error in b

  * relative error in ab or $\dfrac{a}{b}$ = relative error in a + relative error in b

    The latter is an approximate rule of thumb.

Example

The dimensions of a rectangle are given as 23.6 cm and 7.12 cm. Determine:

(a) the absolute error in the perimeter of the rectangle
(b) the percentage relative error in the area of the rectangle.

(a) Absolute error in length is 0.05 cm.
    Absolute error in width is 0.005 cm.
    Absolute error in perimeter is 2(0.05 + 0.005) = 0.11 cm.

(b) Relative error in length is $\dfrac{0.05}{23.6} = 0.002118644$.

   Relative error in width is $\dfrac{0.005}{7.12} = 0.000702247$.

   Relative error in area = 0.002118644 + 0.000702247
   $\qquad\qquad\qquad\qquad = 0.00282$.
   Percentage relative error in area = 0.282%.

Location of roots

If $f(x)$ is continuous, $f(a) < 0$ and $f(b) > 0$ (or $f(a) > 0$ and $f(b) < 0$),
then the equation $f(x) = 0$ has at least one solution (root) between $x = a$ and $x = b$.

Example

If $f(x) = e^x - 2 \cos x$
$f(0) = e^0 - 2 \cos 0 = -1$
$f(1) = e^1 - 2 \cos 1 = 1.64$

Since $f(0) < 0$ and $f(1) > 0$ there is a solution to $e^x - 2 \cos x = 0$ between $x = 0$ and $x = 1$.

Iterative solutions of equations

If the equation $f(x) = 0$ has a rearrangement of the form $x = g(x)$, then the iterative process $x_{r+1} = g(x_r)$, $r = 0, 1, 2, \ldots$ can sometimes be used to find a more accurate approximation to a solution, α, of the equation $f(x) = 0$ if a first approximation x_0 is known (or can be found).

Example

The equation $e^x - 4x = 0$ can be rearranged

to give $x = \dfrac{e^x}{4}$.

The iteration $x_{r+1} = \dfrac{e^{x_r}}{4}$ with $x_0 = 0.4$

gives:

x_1	x_2	x_3	x_4	x_5	x_6	x_7	x_8	x_9	x_{10}
0.37296	0.36301	0.35941	0.35812	0.35766	0.35749	0.35744	0.35741	0.35741	0.35740

Note that the value given on the calculator is used to find the next value even though a 5 d.p. answer is written down.

This appears to suggest that $x = 0.357$ (3 d.p.) is a solution of the equation $e^x - 4x = 0$.

Newton–Raphson procedure

If a is an approximation to a root, α, of the equation $f(x) = 0$, then $a - \dfrac{f(a)}{f'(a)}$ is usually a better approximation.

Example

Returning to the earlier example of the equation $e^x - 4x = 0$ using $x_0 = 0.4$ as before.

This gives the same answer as before but much more quickly.

$$f'(x) = e^x - 4$$

$$x_1 = 0.4 - \frac{e^{0.4} - 4 \times 0.4}{e^{0.4} - 4}$$

$$= 0.35687 \text{ (5 d.p.)}$$

$$x_2 = 0.35687 - \frac{e^{0.35687} - 4 \times 0.35687}{e^{0.35687} - 4}$$

$$= 0.35740 \text{ (5 d.p.)}$$

This value is actually correct to 5 d.p. after only two applications of the Newton–Raphson procedure.

Questions

1 When two resistors with resistances R_1 ohms and R_2 ohms, respectively, are connected in parallel, the new equivalent resistance R ohms is given by $\dfrac{1}{R} = \dfrac{1}{R_1} + \dfrac{1}{R_2}$.

Given that $R_1 = 3.2$ and $R_2 = 7.9$, with each value accurate to one decimal place:

(a) Find the greatest possible value of $\dfrac{1}{R}$.

(b) Find the least possible value of R.

2 The radius of a sphere is found to be 6.2 cm to the nearest mm. Find the absolute error if the volume of the sphere is calculated.

3 The dimensions of a cuboid are 4.2 cm, 5.8 cm and 6.4 cm with each measurement given to the nearest 0.2 cm. Find:

(a) The absolute error in calculating the surface area.

(b) The relative error in calculating the volume.

4 The percentage relative errors in two lengths l_1 and l_2 are 2% and 3%, respectively.

Find an estimate for the percentage relative error in $\dfrac{l_1^2}{l_2^3}$.

5 (a) Show that the equation $x^2 - 3x + 1 = 0$ has a solution between $x = 2.3$ and $x = 2.9$.

(b) Show that the equation can be rearranged to the form $x = 3 - \dfrac{1}{x}$.

(c) Use this rearrangement and the initial value $x_0 = 2.3$ to find the solution to the equation between 2.3 and 2.9. Give your answer to 2 decimal places.

6 The equation $x^3 + 2x - 4 = 0$ has a solution near $x = 1$.

(a) Use the iteration $x_{r+1} = \dfrac{1}{2}[4 - (x_r)^3]$ with initial value $x_0 = 1$ to find the next six terms of the iteration. Explain what is happening.

(b) Show that the equation can also be rearranged to give the iteration
$$x_{r+1} = \sqrt[3]{(4 - 2x_r)}.$$

(c) Use this iteration with $x_0 = 1$ to find the solution of the equation near $x = 1$. Give your answer to 2 decimal places.

7 (a) Show that $y = 4 - x^2$ and $y = e^x$ meet twice by sketching their graphs on the same axes, and hence deduce that $x^2 + e^x - 4 = 0$ has one negative and one positive solution.

(b) Show that the equation $x^2 + e^x - 4 = 0$ has a solution between $x = 1$ and $x = 2$.

(c) Use the iteration $x_{r+1} = -\sqrt{4 - e^{x_r}}$ with $x_0 = -2$ to find an approximation to the negative solution of the equation $x^2 + e^x - 4 = 0$ giving your answer to 3 decimal places.

(d) Use the Newton–Raphson approach with $x_0 = 1.3$ to find an approximation to the root between $x = 1$ and $x = 2$ giving your answer to 4 decimal places.

Vectors

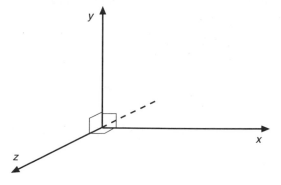

- A scalar has size but no direction.

- A vector has magnitude (size) and direction.

- Three-dimensional vectors are written in the form $a\mathbf{i} + b\mathbf{j} + c\mathbf{k}$ or $\begin{pmatrix} a \\ b \\ c \end{pmatrix}$ where $\mathbf{i}$, $\mathbf{j}$ and $\mathbf{k}$ are unit vectors (vectors of magnitude 1) parallel to the x, y and z-axes, respectively.

- Vectors can be added and subtracted.

$$\begin{pmatrix} a_1 \\ b_1 \\ c_1 \end{pmatrix} \pm \begin{pmatrix} a_2 \\ b_2 \\ c_2 \end{pmatrix} = \begin{pmatrix} a_1 \pm a_2 \\ b_1 \pm b_2 \\ c_1 \pm c_2 \end{pmatrix} = (a_1 \pm a_2)\mathbf{i} + (b_1 \pm b_2)\mathbf{j} + (c_1 \pm c_2)\mathbf{k}$$

Example

$(2\mathbf{i} + 3\mathbf{j} - 4\mathbf{k}) + (-\mathbf{i} + 2\mathbf{j} + 2\mathbf{k}) = (2 + (-1))\,\mathbf{i} + (3 + 2)\,\mathbf{j} + (-4 + 2)\,\mathbf{k} = \mathbf{i} + 5\mathbf{j} - 2\mathbf{k}$

- The modulus (or magnitude or size) of a vector $\mathbf{v} = a\mathbf{i} + b\mathbf{j} + c\mathbf{k}$ is given by $|\mathbf{v}| = \sqrt{a^2 + b^2 + c^2}$

Example

$|2\mathbf{i} - 3\mathbf{j} + 4\mathbf{k}| = \sqrt{2^2 + (-3)^2 + 4^2} = \sqrt{4 + 9 + 16} = \sqrt{29}$

- Two vectors $\mathbf{c}$ and $\mathbf{d}$ are parallel if and only if $\mathbf{c} = \lambda\mathbf{d}$ where λ is a scalar.

Example

The vectors $\mathbf{i} + 2\mathbf{j} - 3\mathbf{k}$ and $3\mathbf{i} + 6\mathbf{j} - 9\mathbf{k}$ are parallel because $3\mathbf{i} + 6\mathbf{j} - 9\mathbf{k} = 3(\mathbf{i} + 2\mathbf{j} - 3\mathbf{k})$

Vector equations of lines

- The vector $\overrightarrow{OA}$, where O is the origin, is called the **position vector** of A and is often written as $\mathbf{a}$ or $\mathbf{r}_A$.

- The **vector equation** of the line going through A and parallel to the vector $\mathbf{b}$ is given by $\mathbf{r} = \mathbf{a} + t\mathbf{b}$ where t is a **scalar variable**. As t varies so all the points on the line are traced.

Note the difference between the vector $\overrightarrow{AB}$ and the vector equation of the line through A and B.

Example

Find the vector equation of the line joining the points A and B where $\mathbf{a} = \overrightarrow{OA} = 3\mathbf{i} - \mathbf{j} + 2\mathbf{k}$ and $\mathbf{b} = \overrightarrow{OB} = 2\mathbf{i} + \mathbf{j} - 4\mathbf{k}$.

$$\overrightarrow{AB} = \overrightarrow{OB} - \overrightarrow{OA} = -\mathbf{i} + 2\mathbf{j} - 6\mathbf{k}$$

$$\mathbf{r}_{AB} = 3\mathbf{i} - \mathbf{j} + 2\mathbf{k} + t(-\mathbf{i} + 2\mathbf{j} - 6\mathbf{k})$$

The vector $\overrightarrow{AB}$ is parallel to the line.

Example

Find the cartesian equation of the line through A and B given above.

$$x\mathbf{i} + y\mathbf{j} + 2\mathbf{k} = 3\mathbf{i} - \mathbf{j} + 2\mathbf{k} + t(-\mathbf{i} + 2\mathbf{j} - 6\mathbf{k})$$

So
$$\left. \begin{array}{l} x = 3 - t \\ y = -1 + 2t \\ z = 2 - 6t \end{array} \right\} \text{equating } \mathbf{i}, \mathbf{j} \text{ and } \mathbf{k} \text{ components.}$$

$$\left. \begin{array}{l} t = 3 - x \\ t = \dfrac{y + 1}{2} \\ t = \dfrac{2 - z}{6} \end{array} \right\} \text{rearranging to make } t \text{ the subject of each one.}$$

So $\quad 3 - x = \dfrac{y + 1}{2} = \dfrac{2 - z}{6} \quad$ is the cartesian equation.

Where two lines meet

- Two lines in three dimensions either:

  (1) intersect
  (2) are parallel
  (3) are not parallel but don't intersect either.

  In case (3) the lines are said to be **skew**.

- To find where (and whether) two lines meet, equate the $\mathbf{i}$, $\mathbf{j}$ and $\mathbf{k}$ components. This gives three pairs of equations in two variables.
  Solve one pair.
  If these values satisfy the third pair then the lines do meet and the position vector of intersection can be found by substitution.

Example

Find the position vector of the point of intersection of the two lines:

$$\mathbf{r} = \mathbf{i} + 2\mathbf{j} - 3\mathbf{k} + t(\mathbf{i} - \mathbf{j} + 2\mathbf{k})$$
and $\quad \mathbf{r} = \quad \mathbf{j} + \mathbf{k} + s(2\mathbf{i} \quad - 2\mathbf{k})$

$$\begin{array}{ll} 1 + t = 0 + 2s & \text{(1) equating } \mathbf{i} \text{ components.} \\ 2 - t = 1 & \text{(2) equating } \mathbf{j} \text{ components.} \\ -3 + 2t = 1 - 2s & \text{(3) equating } \mathbf{k} \text{ components.} \end{array}$$

From (2) $t = 1$
Using $t = 1$ in (1) gives $s = 1$.
Using $t = 1$ in (3) gives $s = 1$.

Putting $t = 1$ in the original equation gives

$\overrightarrow{OP} = 2\mathbf{i} + \mathbf{j} - \mathbf{k}$ for the position vector of the point of intersection.

The scalar product

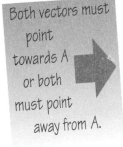

The scalar product is also known as the dot product.

- The scalar product $\mathbf{a} \cdot \mathbf{b}$ is defined by

$$\mathbf{a} \cdot \mathbf{b} = |\mathbf{a}||\mathbf{b}|\cos\theta,$$

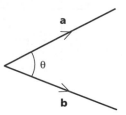

where θ is the angle between the vectors $\mathbf{a}$ and $\mathbf{b}$ when they are both approaching the same point or both leaving the same point.

- If $\quad \mathbf{a} = l_1\mathbf{i} + m_1\mathbf{j} + n_1\mathbf{k}$ and $\mathbf{b} = l_2\mathbf{i} + m_2\mathbf{j} + n_2\mathbf{k}$

  then $\quad \mathbf{a} \cdot \mathbf{b} = l_1l_2 + m_1m_2 + n_1n_2$.

- If $\quad \mathbf{a} \cdot \mathbf{b} = 0$ then $\mathbf{a}$ and $\mathbf{b}$ are perpendicular.

Example

A and B have position vectors $2\mathbf{i} + \mathbf{j} - 3\mathbf{k}$ and $5\mathbf{i} - 2\mathbf{j} + \mathbf{k}$ respectively relative to the origin, O. Find angle OAB to the nearest degree.

$$\begin{aligned}
\overrightarrow{BA} &= (2\mathbf{i} + \mathbf{j} - 3\mathbf{k}) - (5\mathbf{i} - 2\mathbf{j} + \mathbf{k}) \\
&= -3\mathbf{i} + 3\mathbf{j} - 4\mathbf{k} \\
\overrightarrow{OA} \cdot \overrightarrow{BA} &= (2\mathbf{i} + \mathbf{j} - 3\mathbf{k}) \cdot (3\mathbf{i} - 3\mathbf{j} + 4\mathbf{k}) \\
&= 6 + 3 + 12 = 9 \\
|\overrightarrow{OA}| &= \sqrt{2^2 + 1^2 + (-3)^2} = \sqrt{14} \\
|\overrightarrow{BA}| &= \sqrt{(-3)^2 + 3^2 + (-4)^2} = \sqrt{34} \\
\cos\angle OAB &= \frac{\overrightarrow{OB} \cdot \overrightarrow{BA}}{|\overrightarrow{OA}||\overrightarrow{BA}|} = \frac{9}{\sqrt{14}\sqrt{34}} \\
\angle OAB &= 66°
\end{aligned}$$

Both vectors must point towards A or both must point away from A.

Example

Find the acute angle between the two lines in the earlier example.

$$(\mathbf{i} - \mathbf{j} + 2\mathbf{k}) \cdot (2\mathbf{i} - 2\mathbf{k}) = 2 \times 1 - 2 \times 2 = -2$$

$$\left|\mathbf{i} - \mathbf{j} + 2\mathbf{k}\right| = \sqrt{1^2 + 1^2 + 2^2} = \sqrt{6}$$

$$\left|2\mathbf{i} - 2\mathbf{k}\right| = \sqrt{2^2 + 2^2} = \sqrt{8}$$

So $\quad -2 = \sqrt{6}\sqrt{8}\cos\theta$

$$\cos\theta = \frac{-2}{\sqrt{6}\sqrt{8}}$$

$$\theta = 73.2°$$

Be careful to find the angle between the direction parts of the line.

As it stands this will give the obtuse angle. We want the acute angle so ignore the minus sign and calculate

$$\cos^{-1}\frac{2}{\sqrt{6}\sqrt{8}}.$$

Questions

1 Find the modulus of the vector $2\mathbf{i} + \mathbf{j} - 7\mathbf{k}$.

2 Show that the vectors $\overrightarrow{BA}$ and $\overrightarrow{AC}$ are parallel given that

$$\mathbf{a} = \begin{pmatrix} 1 \\ 2 \\ 3 \end{pmatrix}, \mathbf{b} = \begin{pmatrix} -1 \\ -1 \\ -6 \end{pmatrix} \text{ and } \mathbf{c} = \begin{pmatrix} 5 \\ 8 \\ 21 \end{pmatrix}.$$

What can you deduce about B, A and C?

3 Find the vector equation of the line going through the points $A(6, 2, 1)$ and $B(5, 4, 3)$ and show that the point $C(9, -4, -5)$ lies on this line.

4 Find the cartesian equation of the line in question 3.

5 Find a vector equation for the line

$$\frac{x-3}{2} = y = \frac{z+1}{3}.$$

6 The lines l and m have vector equations

$\mathbf{r} = 2\mathbf{i} + 6\mathbf{j} + 7\mathbf{k} + t(\mathbf{i} - 2\mathbf{j} - \mathbf{k})$ and
$\mathbf{r} = 5\mathbf{i} + 2\mathbf{j} + \mathbf{k} + s(\mathbf{i} - \mathbf{j} + 2\mathbf{k})$

(a) Show that l and m meet and find the position vector of their point of intersection.
(b) Calculate the acute angle between l and m.

7 The points A, B, and C have position vectors $2\mathbf{i} + 2\mathbf{j}$, $-7\mathbf{i} + 4\mathbf{j}$ and $\mathbf{i} + 6\mathbf{j}$. Show that the triangle ABC is right-angled and determine where the right angle is.

8 For each of the pairs of lines below determine whether:

(i)   they intersect;
(ii) they are skew;
(iii) they are perpendicular.

(a) $\mathbf{r} = 3\mathbf{i} + 2\mathbf{j} + s(\mathbf{i} - 2\mathbf{j})$
     $\mathbf{r} = 2\mathbf{i} - \mathbf{j} + t(\mathbf{i} + 4\mathbf{j})$

(b) $\mathbf{r} = 3\mathbf{i} + 5\mathbf{j} + u(3\mathbf{i} + \mathbf{j})$
     $\mathbf{r} = -2\mathbf{i} + 7\mathbf{j} + v(\mathbf{i} - 3\mathbf{j})$

(c) $\mathbf{r} = 6\mathbf{i} + 4\mathbf{j} + \mathbf{k} + s(2\mathbf{i} + \mathbf{j} + \mathbf{k})$
     $\mathbf{r} = 4\mathbf{i} - \mathbf{j} + 3\mathbf{k} + t(2\mathbf{i} + \mathbf{j} - 2\mathbf{k})$

Probability

- If an experiment has n equally likely outcomes, the probability of any one of them occurring is $\dfrac{1}{n}$.

- If an event, A, consists of r of these n possible outcomes then the probability of A is given by

    $P(A) = \dfrac{r}{n}$.

- Remember that $0 \leq P(A) \leq 1$.

- Probabilities should always be given as fractions, decimals or percentages.

Example

If an icosohedral die (20 faces) is rolled the probability of obtaining a prime number is $\dfrac{8}{20} = \dfrac{2}{5}$, since 8 of the 20 outcomes (2, 3, 5, 7, 11, 13, 17, 19) are prime numbers.

Complementary events

The symbol A' (or $\overline{A}$) is used for the event that is the **complement** of A (i.e. not A).

$P(A') = 1 - P(A)$

Addition law

$P(A \cup B) = P(A) + P(B) - P(A \cap B)$

A or B (or both)   A and B

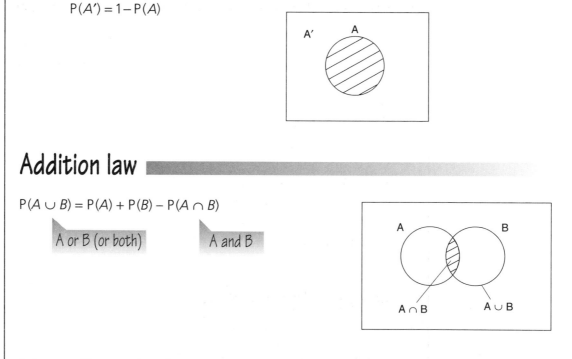

Mutually exclusive events

Two events A and B are said to be **mutually exclusive** if and only if $P(A \cap B) = 0$ i.e. both A and B cannot happen together.

Conditional probability

The **conditional probability** of B given that A has happened is given by:

$$P(B \mid A) = \frac{P(A \cap B)}{P(A)}$$

↗ B given A

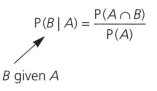
The probability of both divided by the probability you are given.

This can be rewritten as $P(A \cap B) = P(A) P(B \mid A)$.

Independent events

Two events A and B are **independent** if and only if $P(B \mid A) = P(B)$.

From the previous section an equivalent condition for independence is that $P(A \cap B) = P(A) P(B)$.

This means that whether or not A happens the probability of B is unchanged.

Example

Three events A, B and C are such that $P(A) = \frac{3}{5}$, $P(B) = \frac{2}{7}$, $P(A \cup B) = \frac{5}{7}$, $P(C) = \frac{1}{7}$, $P(A \cup C) = \frac{26}{35}$, $P(B \cap C) = \frac{1}{35}$.

(a) Find $P(A \cap B)$.
(b) Determine whether A and B are independent.
(c) Show that A and C are mutually exclusive.
(d) Given that C has happened, find the probability that B happens.

(a) $P(A \cap B) = P(A) + P(B) - P(A \cup B)$

$$= \frac{3}{5} + \frac{2}{7} - \frac{5}{7} = \frac{6}{35}$$

This is a rearrangement of the addition law.

(b) $P(A) P(B) = \frac{3}{5} \times \frac{2}{7} = \frac{6}{35} = P(A \cap B)$

so A and B are independent.

(c) $P(A \cap C) = P(A) + P(C) - P(A \cup C)$

$$= \frac{3}{5} + \frac{1}{7} - \frac{26}{35} = 0$$

so A and C are mutually exclusive.

(d) $P(B \mid C) = \frac{P(B \cap C)}{P(C)} = \frac{\frac{1}{35}}{\frac{1}{7}} = \frac{1}{5}$.

Possibility space diagrams

- Possibility space diagrams can be used to illustrate situations involving two experiments.

Example

Two fair die, one a cube and one a tetrahedron, are rolled. What is the probability of scoring a sum of more than five on the two die?

The scores giving the required condition are ringed by the dots.

+	1	2	3	4	5	6
1	2	3	4	5	6	7
2	3	4	5	6	7	8
3	4	5	6	7	8	9
4	5	6	7	8	9	10

Cubical die

Tetrahedral die

The sums are written in the body of the table.

14 outcomes have a sum greater than 5.

$$P \text{ (sum more than five)} = \frac{14}{24} = \frac{7}{12}.$$

There are 24 equally likely outcomes.

Tree diagrams

- Tree diagrams are useful for:
  * illustrating problems
  * calculating probabilities.

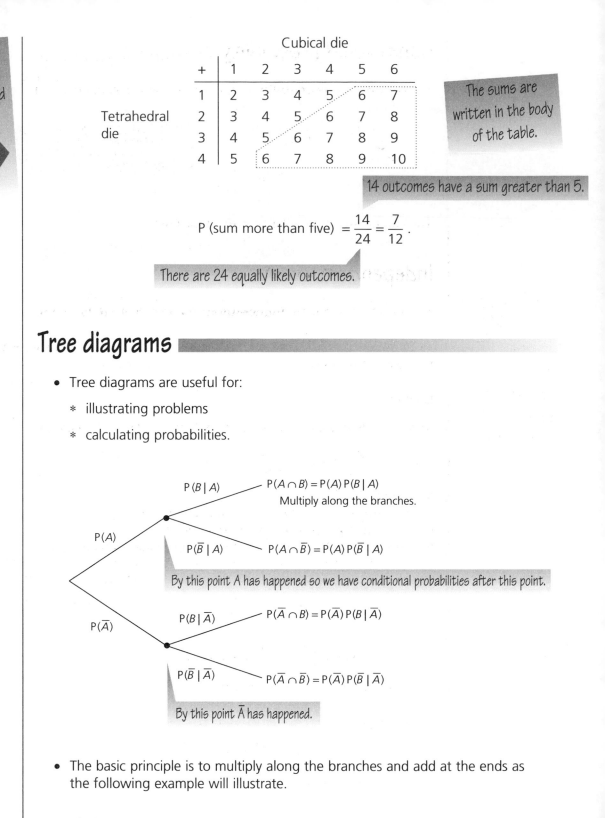

$P(B \mid A)$ — $P(A \cap B) = P(A)\,P(B \mid A)$
Multiply along the branches.

$P(A)$

$P(\overline{B} \mid A)$ — $P(A \cap \overline{B}) = P(A)\,P(\overline{B} \mid A)$

By this point A has happened so we have conditional probabilities after this point.

$P(\overline{A})$

$P(B \mid \overline{A})$ — $P(\overline{A} \cap B) = P(\overline{A})\,P(B \mid \overline{A})$

$P(\overline{B} \mid \overline{A})$ — $P(\overline{A} \cap \overline{B}) = P(\overline{A})\,P(\overline{B} \mid \overline{A})$

By this point $\overline{A}$ has happened.

- The basic principle is to multiply along the branches and add at the ends as the following example will illustrate.

Example

A bag contains 2 red and 5 blue counters. Two counters are randomly selected and removed from the bag. Calculate the probability that the two counters are of different colours.

It is important to note that the counters are removed without replacement. This is clear from the question. Using the notation R_1 for the event. 'The 1st counter is red' and B_2 for the event 'the 2nd counter is blue', etc. We have the following tree diagram:

$$P(B_2 \mid R_1) = \frac{5}{6}$$

$$P(R_1 \cap B_2) = P(R_1)\,P(B_2 \mid R_1) = \frac{2}{7} \times \frac{5}{6}$$

$$P(R_1) = \frac{2}{7}$$

$$P(R_2 \mid R_1) = \frac{1}{6}$$

These two branches could have been omitted altogether as they are irrelevant to what is needed.

$$P(B_2 \mid B_1) = \frac{4}{6}$$

$$P(B_1) = \frac{5}{7}$$

$$P(R_2 \mid B_1) = \frac{2}{6}$$

$$P(B_1 \cap R_2) = P(B_1)\,P(R_2 \mid B_1) = \frac{5}{7} \times \frac{2}{6}$$

We need $P(R_1 \cap B_2) + P(B_1 \cap R_2) = \dfrac{2}{7} \times \dfrac{5}{6} + \dfrac{5}{7} \times \dfrac{2}{6} = \dfrac{10}{21}$.

First one red and second one blue **or** first one blue and second one red.

A few final thoughts

- Try not to become too tied into formulae but think about what is happening first.

- It is important to read probability questions very carefully as a single word can change the question considerably.

- Try and understand clearly how to spot a conditional probability from phrases like 'given that …', 'it is known that when …', 'if the first counter is red …', etc.

- Remember that probabilities are always between 0 and 1 inclusive – never negative, never bigger than 1!

Questions

1. Given that $P(A) = \dfrac{1}{4}$, $P(B) = \dfrac{1}{7}$ and $P(A \mid B) = \dfrac{1}{3}$.

   (a) Find $P(A \cup B)$.
   (b) Explain, giving your reasons, whether or not A and B are independent.

2. It is known that $P(V \cup W) = \dfrac{2}{5}$, $P(V) = \dfrac{1}{10}$ and that V and W are mutually exclusive.

   Find:

   (a) $P(W)$.
   (b) $P(V \mid W)$.

3. Two fair cubical dice are thrown and the numbers uppermost multiplied together.

   (a) Draw up a possibility space diagram to illustrate all the possible outcomes.
   (b) Find the probability that the product of the two scores will be even.
   (c) If it is known that the product is odd what is the probability that both dice show a 3 uppermost.

4. Three players each roll a fair cubical die. Find the probability that:

   (a) They all obtain the same number.
   (b) They all obtain an even number.
   (c) No one obtains a 1 or a 6.

5. A motorist leaves for work on time with probability 0.85. If she leaves on time the probability she will be late is 0.05. If she does not leave on time the corresponding probability is 0.25. Calculate:

   (a) The probability that she will leave on time and arrive at work on time.
   (b) That she will have left on time given that she arrived late for work.

6. Two players fire arrows at a target. The first, Andrea, has a probability of 0.8 of hitting the target with a particular arrow whereas the second, Georgina, has a probability of 0.65 of hitting the target. In order to decide who goes first they cut a pack of cards. If a heart is obtained Georgina goes first. Otherwise Andrea goes first. Find the probability that:

   (a) Georgina goes first and hits the target.
   (b) The first shot misses the target.
   (c) Andrea went first given that the first shot hits the target.

Statistics

Presentation of data

- It is important to choose an appropriate diagram for a particular type of data.
- Bar charts, pie charts and line diagrams are used for categorical or discrete numerical data.
- Histograms and cumulative frequency curves are used for grouped discrete or continuous data.

Histogram

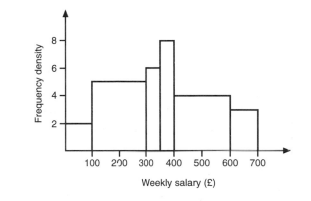

- The histogram above shows the weekly salaries of 3000 people.
- The height of the bars is the frequency density $= \dfrac{\text{Frequency}}{\text{Class size}}$.
- It is the area of each bar that represents the frequency.

Example

There are $200 \times 5 = 1000$ people with a weekly salary between £100 and £300.

Cumulative frequency curves

From the previous example we have:

Weekly salary (£)	$0 \leq x < 100$	$100 \leq x < 300$	$300 \leq x < 350$	$350 \leq x < 400$	$400 \leq x < 600$	$600 \leq x \leq 700$
Frequency	200	1000	300	400	800	300
Cumulative frequency	200	1200	1500	1900	2700	3000

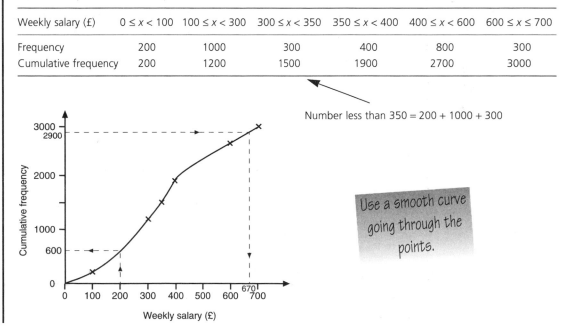

Number less than $350 = 200 + 1000 + 300$

Use a smooth curve going through the points.

Read up and across or across and down as appropriate.

- The cumulative frequencies are plotted against the upper class boundaries, i.e. 100, 300, 350, 400, 600, 700.
- A **cumulative frequency polygon** has the curve replaced by a series of straight lines joining the points.
- Information can be read off the graph.

Example

- There are 600 people with a weekly salary of £200 or less.
- The weekly salary above which only 100 people are paid is £670.

Measures of location

- These are often known as **averages** and give a typical value of the population.
- The **mode** is the most common value – the one with the greatest frequency. For grouped data the modal class is the class with the greatest frequency.
- The **median** is the middle value when the data are arranged in increasing order of size. The median can be estimated from a cumulative frequency curve by reading across and down from half the total frequency.

Example

Our earlier cumulative frequency example gives a median of 350 if you read across and down from half of 3000 (i.e. 1500).

- The **mean** is obtained using the formula:

$$\bar{x} = \frac{\Sigma f \, x}{\Sigma f}$$

Multiply each value by its frequency, add them together and divide by the total frequency.

For grouped data use the mid-point of each group as the *x*-values.

Example

For our cumulative frequency example above:

$$\bar{x} = \frac{200 \times 50 + 1000 \times 200 + 300 \times 325 + 400 \times 375 + 800 \times 500 + 300 \times 650}{200 + 1000 + 300 + 400 + 800 + 300}$$

$$= \frac{1052500}{3000}$$

Your calculator may be able to work the mean out if the data is entered in.

$$= £350.83 \text{ (to the nearest penny)}.$$

Remember to write the answer in context.

Measures of dispersion (spread)

- These show how spread out a set of data is. The greater the measure the more spread out the data is.
- Range = largest value – smallest value.
- Interquartile range = upper quartile – lower quartile.

The **lower quartile** is the value that is one-quarter of the way through the data.
The **upper quartile** is the value that is three-quarters of the way through the data.

Example

In our earlier example:

$\frac{1}{4}$ of 3000 = 750 and $\frac{3}{4}$ of 3000 = 2250.

The lower quartile is approximately £220 (read across from 750 and down) and the upper quartile is approximately £490 (read across from 2250 and down). The interquartile range = 490 − 220 = £270 approximately.

- Variance = $\sigma^2 = \dfrac{\sum f(x - \bar{x})^2}{\sum f}$

Square the difference between each value and the mean, multiply by the frequency, add together and divide by the total frequency.

This form can be thought of as the mean of the squares – square of the mean.

This can also be rewritten in the computationally easier form

Variance = $\sigma^2 = \dfrac{\sum f x^2}{\sum f} - \bar{x}^2$

Square each value times by the frequency, add together and divide by the total frequency, then subtract the square of the mean.

Your calculator may do this for you as well. Find out how!

Again for grouped data use the mid-point of each group as the x-value.

Example

In our example:

Variance

$$= \frac{200 \times 50^2 + 1000 \times 200^2 + 300 \times 325^2 + 400 \times 375^2 + 800 \times 500^2 + 300 \times 650^2}{200 + 1000 + 300 + 400 + 800 + 300} - 350.83^2$$

$$= \frac{455187500}{3000} - 350.83^2$$

$$= 28645.13891$$

- The standard deviation, $\sigma = \sqrt{\text{Variance}}$.

Example

In our example:

$\sigma = \sqrt{28645.13891} = £169.25.$

The units for the standard deviation are the same as the original data.

Question

1 The sale price of 10100 different homes in a certain location are recorded and the following results obtained:

Sale price (£)	$0 \leq x < 40000$	$40000 \leq x < 50000$	$50000 \leq x < 55000$	$55000 \leq x < 60000$
Frequency	1700	2800	1700	1200

Sale price (£)	$60000 \leq x < 70000$	$70000 \leq x < 85000$	$85000 \leq x \leq 110000$
Frequency	950	630	1120

(a) Draw a histogram for the data.
(b) Draw a cumulative frequency curve for the data.
(c) Use your cumulative frequency curve to form estimates for the median and interquartile range.
(d) Calculate estimates for the mean and standard deviation of the sale prices of these houses.

Answers

Algebraic skills

1 (a) $\dfrac{4(x-1)}{x(x-2)}$

   (b) $6x^4 + 4x^3 - 23x^2 - 6x + 21$

   (c) $\dfrac{2x^2 + 4x + 3}{(x+1)(x-1)(2x+3)}$

   (d) $\dfrac{x(2x+7)}{(x+2)^2}$

2 (a) $(x+2y)(3x+7)$

   (b) $(4x-3)^2$

   (c) $2xy(4x + 3y - 7x^2y^2)$

   (d) $(3x-11)(2x+3)$

   (e) $(3x+2y)(3x-2y)$

   (f) $\left(\sqrt{x}-4\right)\left(\sqrt{x}+1\right)$

3 (a) $x = 7y^4 + 42y^2 + 61$

   (b) $x = \dfrac{7(y-1)}{2y+3}$

4 (a) $8\sqrt{5}$

   (b) $9\sqrt{2}$

   (c) $\dfrac{24\sqrt{6}-21}{67}$

   (d) $10\sqrt{14}+42$

5 $3x^3 + 8x^2 + 13x + 26$ remainder 53

6 (a) 50

   (b) 838

7 (a) $(x+1)(x+4)(2x-3)$

   (b) $(x-2)(x+3)(3x+1)$

8 $3(-1)^3 - 6(-1)^2 + a(-1) - 1 = 2(3 \times 3^3 - 6 \times 3^2 + 3a - 1)$

$$-3 - 6 - a - 1 = 162 - 108 + 6a - 2$$
$$7a = -62$$
$$a = -8\frac{6}{7}$$

9 (a) $\dfrac{3}{2x-1} - \dfrac{2}{x+2}$

   (b) $\dfrac{3}{x+1} + \dfrac{2x+7}{x^2+x+1}$

   (c) $\dfrac{3}{x} + \dfrac{3}{x-1} + \dfrac{2}{(x-1)^2}$

   (d) $3x + 7 + \dfrac{3}{x+1} + \dfrac{2}{x-2}$

   (e) $\dfrac{x^2 + 3x - 13}{(x+2)(x-1)} = \dfrac{x^2 + 3x - 13}{x^2 + x - 2}$

$$= 1 + \dfrac{2x - 11}{x^2 + x - 2}$$
$$= 1 + \dfrac{2x - 1}{(x+2)(x-1)}$$
$$= 1 + \dfrac{5}{x+2} - \dfrac{3}{x-1}$$

Functions

1 $f(x)$ is many to one since $x = 4$ gives $y = \pm 2$.

2 (a) yes (b) yes (c) no (d) no

3 (a) $1 \le f(x) \le 81$ (b) $0 < f(x) < 1$

   (c) $-\infty < f(x) < \infty$ (d) $0 \le f(x) \le 8$

> Hint: sketches are essential in many problems of this kind.

4 (a) (b)

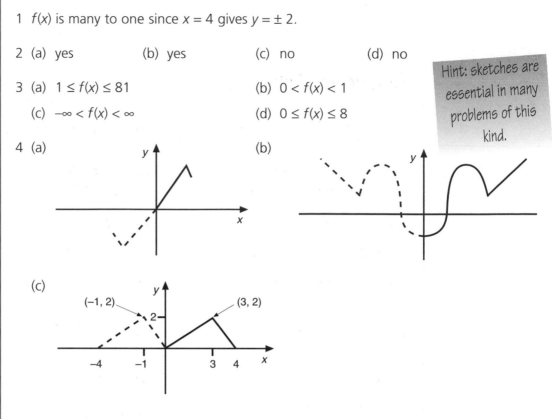

   (c)

5 (a) Translate 5 units in the negative x-direction, reflect in the x-axis, translate 7 units down parallel to the y-axis.

   (b) Stretch scale factor 2 parallel to the x-axis, stretch scale factor ⅓ parallel to the y-axis.

6 (a) $fg(x) = x^3 - 7$ (b) $g_o h(x) = x^{3/2}$ (c) $g^2(x) = x^9$

   (d) $ff(x) = x - 14$ (e) $hgf(x) = \sqrt{(x - 7)^3}$

7 $f^{-1}(x)\,\dfrac{3x + 1}{x - 2},\ x > 2$

8 (a) $v^2(x) = x$; (b) v is self-inversing; $v^{-1}: x \to \dfrac{x}{x - 1}$

Equations and inequalities

1 (a) $x = \dfrac{38}{23}$ (b) $x = \dfrac{4}{3}$ (c) $x = \dfrac{1}{3}$ or $x = \dfrac{7}{3}$

2 (a) $x = -\dfrac{1}{3}$ or 3.5

   (b) $x = -3$ or 1

   (c) $x = \pm\dfrac{3}{2}$

   (d) $x = 0.382$ or 2.618

3 Let speed they normally walk be v km/h.

$$\frac{1}{v} - \frac{1}{v+1} = \frac{1}{20}$$

> Using time $= \dfrac{distance}{speed}$
>
> and 3 minutes $= \dfrac{1}{20}$ hour.

$$20\,(v+1) - 20v = v\,(v+1)$$

$$v^2 + v - 20 = 0$$

> Multiply through by $20\,v\,(v+1)$.

$$v = 4\,\text{km/h} \qquad \text{since} \qquad v > 0$$

4 (a) $x < 4$ (b) $x < 1$ (c) $x \le -\dfrac{16}{3}$ or $x \ge 4$

   (d) $x < \dfrac{5}{6}$

5 (a) $-\dfrac{1}{6} < x < \dfrac{3}{2}$ (b) $-2 \le x \le -\dfrac{3}{2}$ or $x \ge 1$ (c) $-10 < x < -1$

6 (a) $x = 3$ and $y = -7$ (b) $x = 2$ and $y = 5$
                                      or $x = -13$ and $y = -5$

7 (a) 2, no   (b) 1, yes   (c) 2, yes   (d) none, no

8 (a)

$y = x^2 - 5x + 4$, vertex $(2.5, -2.25)$, intercepts at 1 and 4, y-intercept 4.

   (b)

$y = 7 + 13x - 2x^2$, vertex $(3.25, 28.125)$, intercepts at $-\dfrac{1}{2}$ and 7, y-intercept 7.

Indices and logarithms

1 (a) $\dfrac{1}{5}$ (b) 8   (c) $\dfrac{1}{y}$

    (d) $\dfrac{x}{x-1}$ (e) $\dfrac{3}{4}$ (f) 7

    (g) log 6   (h) log 5   (i) log $(x-1)$

2

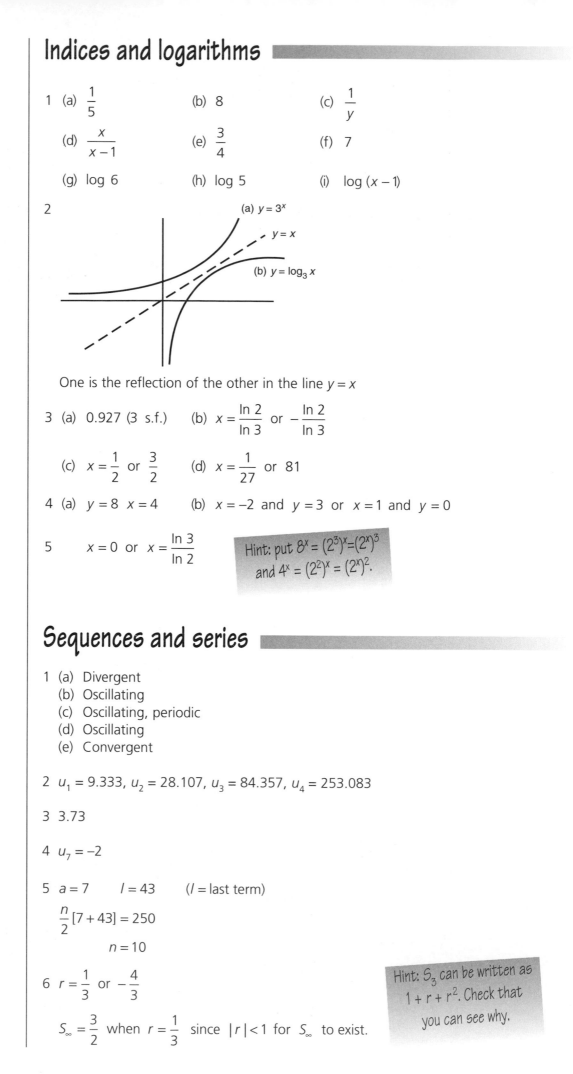

(a) $y = 3^x$

$y = x$

(b) $y = \log_3 x$

One is the reflection of the other in the line $y = x$

3 (a) 0.927 (3 s.f.)   (b) $x = \dfrac{\ln 2}{\ln 3}$ or $-\dfrac{\ln 2}{\ln 3}$

    (c) $x = \dfrac{1}{2}$ or $\dfrac{3}{2}$ (d) $x = \dfrac{1}{27}$ or 81

4 (a) $y = 8$ $x = 4$ (b) $x = -2$ and $y = 3$ or $x = 1$ and $y = 0$

5     $x = 0$ or $x = \dfrac{\ln 3}{\ln 2}$

> Hint: put $8^x = (2^3)^x = (2^x)^3$
> and $4^x = (2^2)^x = (2^x)^2$.

Sequences and series

1 (a) Divergent
   (b) Oscillating
   (c) Oscillating, periodic
   (d) Oscillating
   (e) Convergent

2 $u_1 = 9.333$, $u_2 = 28.107$, $u_3 = 84.357$, $u_4 = 253.083$

3 3.73

4 $u_7 = -2$

5 $a = 7$ $l = 43$ (l = last term)

   $\dfrac{n}{2}[7 + 43] = 250$

          $n = 10$

6 $r = \dfrac{1}{3}$ or $-\dfrac{4}{3}$

   $S_\infty = \dfrac{3}{2}$ when $r = \dfrac{1}{3}$ since $|r| < 1$ for S_∞ to exist.

> Hint: S_3 can be written as
> $1 + r + r^2$. Check that
> you can see why.

7 (a) $243 - 810x + 1080x^2 - 720x^3$ $x \in \mathbb{R}$

(b) $3^{-\frac{1}{4}}\left(1 + \dfrac{x}{12} + \dfrac{5x^2}{288} + \dfrac{5x^3}{1152}\right)$ $|x| < 3$

(c) $4x - \dfrac{32}{3}x^3$ $x \in \mathbb{R}$

Hint: Find series for $\ln(1 + 2x)$ and multiply by $(x - 1)$.

(d) $-2x + 4x^2 - \dfrac{14x^3}{3}$ $-\dfrac{1}{2} < x \leq \dfrac{1}{2}$

(e) $\ln 2 + \left(-\dfrac{3}{2}x - \dfrac{9}{8}x^2 - \dfrac{9}{8}x^3\right)$ $-\dfrac{2}{3} \leq x < \dfrac{2}{3}$

Hint: use laws of logarithms on $\ln\left(2\left(1 - \dfrac{3x}{2}\right)\right)$ first.

(f) $2x - \dfrac{4}{3}x^3$ $x \in \mathbb{R}$

Hint: it is quicker to recognise that $2\sin x \cos x = \sin 2x$.

8 Using $\sqrt{1 + x} = 1 + \dfrac{1}{2}x - \dfrac{1}{8}x^2 + \dfrac{1}{16}x^3$ with $x = 0.02$

gives $\sqrt{1.02} \approx 1.00995$.

Co-ordinate geometry

1 $\sqrt{133}$

2 $(2, 3, 6.5)$

3 M is $(5, -3)$ $AM = \sqrt{116} = 2\sqrt{29}$

4 (a) They meet $\left(\text{gradients } \dfrac{2}{3} \text{ and } -\dfrac{2}{3}\right)$.

(b) They are parallel $\left(\text{gradients are both } \dfrac{1}{2}\right)$.

(c) They are perpendicular and meet $\left(\text{gradients } \dfrac{1}{3} \text{ and } -3\right)$.

5 (a) $y = -7x + 23$
(b) $y = -3x + 19$
(c) $3y = 5x + 15$

6 $(2.5, 0)$ and $\left(0, \dfrac{5}{3}\right)$

7 $\tan\theta = 1\dfrac{3}{4} \Rightarrow \theta = 60.3°$

8

$y = \dfrac{x}{x-1}$

Hint: $\dfrac{x}{x-1} = \dfrac{x-1+1}{x-1} = 1 + \dfrac{1}{x-1}$ so move curve $y = \dfrac{1}{x}$ 1 unit to the right and 1 unit up.

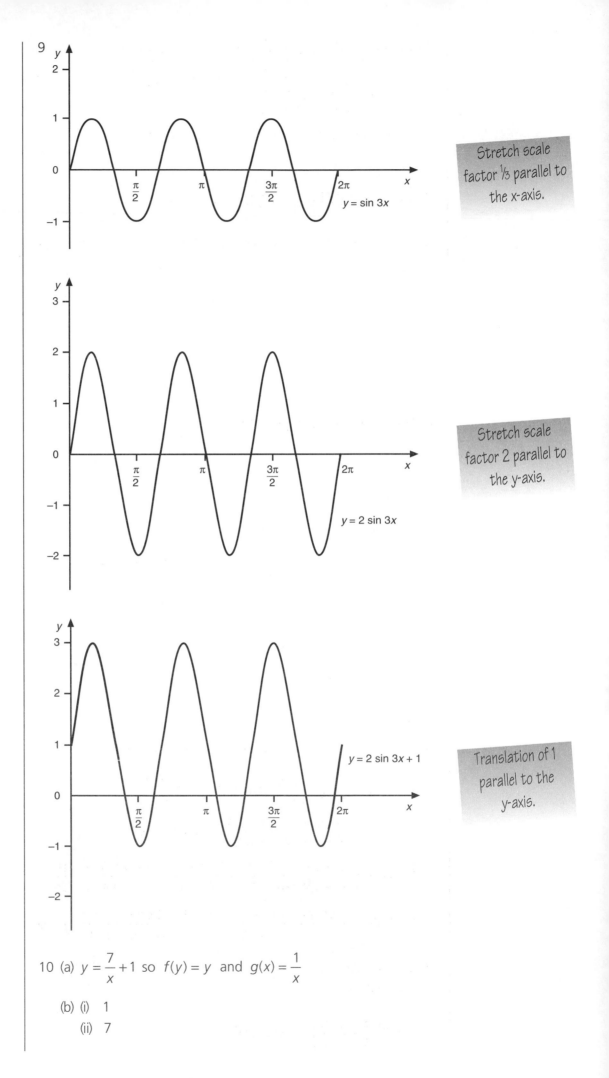

9

$y = \sin 3x$

Stretch scale factor ⅓ parallel to the x-axis.

$y = 2 \sin 3x$

Stretch scale factor 2 parallel to the y-axis.

$y = 2 \sin 3x + 1$

Translation of 1 parallel to the y-axis.

10 (a) $y = \dfrac{7}{x} + 1$ so $f(y) = y$ and $g(x) = \dfrac{1}{x}$

(b) (i) 1

(ii) 7

11 (a)

ln y	0.92	2.26	2.87	3.01	3.25
x	2.39	4.17	7.23	8.19	10.2

(b) $\ln a = 0.69 \Rightarrow a = 2.0$

(c) $\ln b = 0.095 \Rightarrow b = 1.1$

Trigonometry

1 If θ_1 was acute and $\sin \theta_1 = \dfrac{2}{3}$ then $\cos \theta_1 = \dfrac{\sqrt 5}{3}$ from diagram below.

$\Rightarrow \cos\theta = \cos(180 - \theta_1) = -\cos\theta_1 = -\dfrac{\sqrt 5}{3}$

2 (a) $x = 150°$

(b) $x = 0.41,\ 1.68,\ 2.50,\ 3.78,\ 4.60,\ 5.87$ radians

(c) $\theta = \dfrac{\pi}{4}$ radians | Hint: $2\sin\theta\cos\theta = \sin 2\theta$.

(d) $x = 30°,\ 150°$ | Hint: put $\cos 2x = 1 - 2\sin^2 x$.

(e) $\theta = 26.6°$ or $135°$

3 (a) 8.70 km

(b) 046.7°

4

$\cos C = \dfrac{15^2 + 20^2 - 10^2}{2 \times 15 \times 20} \Rightarrow \cos C = 0.875$

$h = 15\sin C = 7.26\,\text{m}$

5 $R\cos t \cos\alpha + R\sin t \sin\alpha = 6\cos t + 2\sin t \quad \Rightarrow \quad R = \sqrt{40} \quad \tan\alpha = \dfrac{1}{3}$

$t = -0.337$ or 0.981

6 $x = 66.7°$

7 (a) $\text{LHS} = 1 - \sin^2 A + 1 - 2\sin^2 A = 2 - 3\sin^2 A = \text{RHS}$

(b) $\text{RHS} = \dfrac{1}{\sin^2 A} - \dfrac{\sin A}{\cos A} = \dfrac{1}{2\sin A \cos A} - \dfrac{\sin A}{\cos A}$

$= \dfrac{1 - 2\sin^2 A}{2\sin A \cos A} = \dfrac{\cos 2A}{\sin 2A} = \cos 2A = \text{RHS}$

(c) $\text{LHS} = \dfrac{\tan 45 + \tan A}{1 - \tan 45 \tan A} \cdot \dfrac{\tan 45 - \tan A}{1 + \tan 45 \tan A} = \dfrac{1 + \tan A}{1 - \tan A} \cdot \dfrac{1 - \tan A}{1 + \tan A} = 1$

(d) $\text{LHS} = \dfrac{\sin\theta(1 + \cos\theta) + \sin\theta(1 - \cos\theta)}{1 - \cos^2 \theta} = \dfrac{2\sin\theta}{\sin^2 \theta} = \dfrac{2}{\sin\theta} = 2\operatorname{cosec}\theta$

8 (a) 7.48 cm²

(b) 10.0 cm²

9 $\dfrac{1}{2} \times 3^2 \left(\dfrac{\pi}{4} - \sin\dfrac{\pi}{4} \right) = 0.352$ cm²

10 (a) If M is the mid-point of AB and N is the mid-point of the base

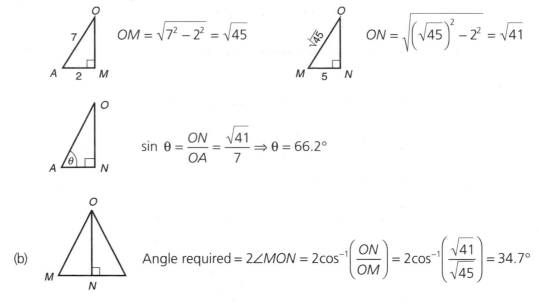

$$OM = \sqrt{7^2 - 2^2} = \sqrt{45}$$

$$ON = \sqrt{\left(\sqrt{45}\right)^2 - 2^2} = \sqrt{41}$$

$$\sin\theta = \frac{ON}{OA} = \frac{\sqrt{41}}{7} \Rightarrow \theta = 66.2°$$

(b) Angle required $= 2\angle MON = 2\cos^{-1}\left(\dfrac{ON}{OM}\right) = 2\cos^{-1}\left(\dfrac{\sqrt{41}}{\sqrt{45}}\right) = 34.7°$

(c) Angle between OA and CD = angle between OA and OB.

$$\cos\alpha = \frac{2}{7} \Rightarrow \alpha = 73.4°$$

Calculus 1: differentiation

1 (a) $3\sec^2 3x$

(b) $\sec^3 x + \sec x \tan^2 x$

(c) $3x^2 \sin x + x^3 \cos x$

(d) $\dfrac{x^2 e^x - 2xe^x}{x^4} = \dfrac{e^x(x-2)}{x^3}$

(e) $\dfrac{x}{\sqrt{x^2 + 1}}$

(f) $-\dfrac{1}{x}\operatorname{cosec}^2(\ln x)$

(g) $(\ln 2)2^x$

(h) $\dfrac{3}{\sqrt{4 - 9x^2}}$

2 (a) $3y^2\dfrac{dy}{dx} + 3x\dfrac{dy}{dx} + 3y = e^x \cos y \dfrac{dy}{dx} + e^x \sin y \Rightarrow \dfrac{dy}{dx} = \dfrac{e^x \sin y - 3y}{3y^2 + 3x - e^x \cos y}$

(b) $\dfrac{dy}{dx} = \dfrac{\cos t + e^{-t}}{3e^t - \sin t}$

(c) $\dfrac{dy}{dx} = \dfrac{2x + 1}{x^2 + x}$

Hint: write as $y = \ln(x^2 + x)$.

(d) $\dfrac{dy}{dx} = \dfrac{1}{n}x^{\frac{1-n}{n}}$

Hint: write as $y = x^{1/n}$.

(e) $\dfrac{dx}{dy} = \sec^2 y \Rightarrow \dfrac{dy}{dx} = \dfrac{1}{\sec^2 y} = \dfrac{1}{1 + \tan^2 y} = \dfrac{1}{1 + x^2}$

3 $\dfrac{dA}{dt} = \pi r \text{ cm}^2/\text{s}$

4 (a) (0, 0) point of inflexion

(2, –64) minimum point

(b) $\left(\dfrac{1}{e}, -\dfrac{1}{e}\right)$ minimum point

5 $2\pi rh + 2\pi r^2 = 600\pi \;\Rightarrow\; h = \dfrac{300}{r} - r$

$v = \pi r^2 h = 300\pi r - \pi r^3$

Radius = 10 cm   Height = 20 cm

Maximum volume = 2000π cm^3

6 (a) Surface area = $2x^2 + 4xh = 600$

$h = \dfrac{600 - 2x^2}{4x}$

Volume $= x^2 h = x^2 \dfrac{(600 - 2x^2)}{4x}$

$= 150x - \dfrac{1}{2}x^3$

(b) $x = 10$ cm

(c) Maximum volume = 1000 cm^3

7 Tangent has equation $y = 5x - 4$

Normal has equation $5y + x = 32$.

8 (a) $\dfrac{dy}{dx} = \dfrac{3t^2}{2t} = \dfrac{3t}{2} \Rightarrow \left.\dfrac{dy}{dx}\right|_{t=2} = 3$

Equation of tangent is $\dfrac{y-8}{x-4} = 3 \Rightarrow y - 8 = 3(x - 4) \Rightarrow y = 3x - 4$

(b) $t^3 = 3t^2 - 4$ putting $y = t^3$ and $x = t^2$

$t^3 - 3t^2 + 4 = 0 \Rightarrow (t - 2)^2(t + 1) = 0$

$t = -1$ Q is $(1, -1)$

Calculus 2: integration

1 (a) $\dfrac{1}{2} \ln(e^{2x} + 3) + c$

Hint: Modulus signs are not needed as $(e^{2x}+3)>0$ for all x.

(b) $\dfrac{2\tan^7 x}{7} + c$

(c) $\dfrac{\pi}{6} + \dfrac{\sqrt{3}}{8}$

(d) $\dfrac{\tan^2 x}{2} - \ln |\sec x| + c$

Hint: write $\tan^3 x = \tan x\,(\sec^2 x - 1)$.

(e) $-\dfrac{\cos 6x}{12} - \dfrac{\cos 2x}{4} + c$

(f) $\dfrac{1}{3}\tan^{-1}\left(\dfrac{3x}{2}\right) + c$

(g) $2 \ln|x-1| + \dfrac{1}{x-1} + c$

Hint: write $2x-3$ as $2(x-1)-1$.

(h) $\ln 12$

(i) $e-2$

Hint: use integration by parts twice.

(j) $\dfrac{1}{4}(\sqrt{3}-1)$

Hint: use the substitution $x = 2\sin\theta$.

(k) $\dfrac{\sqrt{3}}{3}\pi - \ln 2 = 1.12$ (3 s.f.)

Hint: use integration by parts.

(l) $\dfrac{1}{3}(1+x^2)^{3/2} + c$

(m) $\dfrac{x^{n+1}\ln x}{n+1} - \dfrac{x^{n+1}}{(n+1)^2}$

(n) $\dfrac{2}{35}$

2 (a) $\tan^{-1}\left(\dfrac{y}{2}\right) = \ln(x^2+1)$

(b) $2\sqrt{y} = \dfrac{x}{2} + 3\ln|x| + c$

(c) $\dfrac{1}{2}\sin 2y = -\dfrac{1}{3}\ln|x+2| + \dfrac{1}{3}\ln|x-1| + c$

(d) $\tan y = \ln x + \sqrt{3}$

3 $4\sqrt{3}$

Hint : Area $= \int_{-\sqrt{3}}^{\sqrt{3}}\left(-x^2 - 2x + 3\right)\,dx - \int_{-\sqrt{3}}^{\sqrt{3}}\left(-2x\right)\,dx$ since curve and line meet at $x = \pm\sqrt{3}$.

4 $\dfrac{29\pi}{6}$

5 $\displaystyle\int \dfrac{dx}{a-x} = k\,dt$

$-\ln(a-x) = kt + c$

$-\ln a = c$ since $x = 0$ at $t = 0$

$-\ln(a-x) = kt - \ln a$

$\ln a - \ln(a-x) = kt$

$\ln\dfrac{a}{a-x} = kt$

$\dfrac{a}{a-x} = e^{kt}$

$a - x = \dfrac{a}{e^{kt}} = ae^{-kt}$

$x = a - ae^{-kt}$

$x = a(1 - e^{-kt})$

Numerical methods

1 (a) 0.445 (3 d.p.)

Hint: $\frac{1}{x}$ is greatest when x is smallest.

   (b) 2.25 (3 s.f.)

Hint: R is least when $\frac{1}{R}$ is greatest.

2 24.3 cm^3

3 (a) Maximum surface area $= 2 \times 4.3 \times 5.9 + 2 \times 4.3 \times 6.5 + 2 \times 5.9 \times 6.5$
$$= 183.34 \text{ cm}^2$$
      Minimum surface area $= 2 \times 4.1 \times 5.7 + 2 \times 4.1 \times 6.3 + 2 \times 5.7 \times 6.3$
$$= 170.22 \text{ cm}^2$$
      Using giving values surface area $= 2 \times 4.2 \times 5.8 + 2 \times 4.2 \times 6.4 + 2 \times 5.8 \times 6.4$
$$= 176.72 \text{ cm}^2$$
$$\text{Absolute error} = 6.62 \text{ cm}^2$$

   (b) Relative error $= \dfrac{4.3 \times 5.9 \times 6.5 - 4.2 \times 5.8 \times 6.4}{4.2 \times 5.8 \times 6.4}$
$$= 0.0577 \text{ (3 s.f.)}$$

4 13%

5 (a) $2.3^2 - 3 \times 2.3 + 1 = -0.61$ $2.9^2 - 3 \times 2.9 + 1 = 0.71$

      A sign change, so a solution between $x = 2.3$ and $x = 2.9$

   (b) $x^2 = 3x - 1 \;\Rightarrow\; x = \dfrac{3x - 1}{x} = 3 - \dfrac{1}{x}$

   (c) 2.62

6 (a) $x_1 = 1.5$ $x_2 = 0.3125$ $x_3 = 1.9847$ $x_4 = -1.9091$
       $x_5 = 5.4793$ $x_6 = -80.2497$

      The values are not converging.

   (b) $x^3 = 4 - 2x \;\Rightarrow\; x = \sqrt[3]{4 - 2x} \;\Rightarrow\; x_{r+1} = \sqrt[3]{4 - 2x_r}$

   (c) 1.18

7 (a)

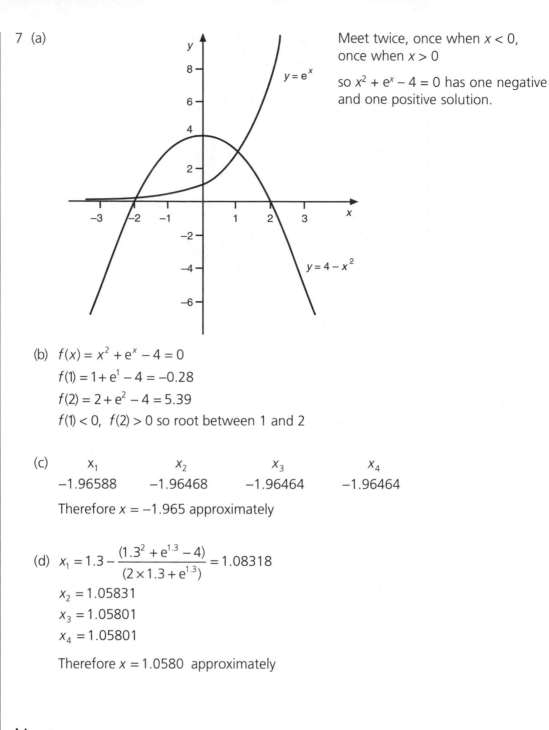

Meet twice, once when $x < 0$, once when $x > 0$

so $x^2 + e^x - 4 = 0$ has one negative and one positive solution.

(b) $f(x) = x^2 + e^x - 4 = 0$

$f(1) = 1 + e^1 - 4 = -0.28$

$f(2) = 2 + e^2 - 4 = 5.39$

$f(1) < 0$, $f(2) > 0$ so root between 1 and 2

(c)

x_1	x_2	x_3	x_4
-1.96588	-1.96468	-1.96464	-1.96464

Therefore $x = -1.965$ approximately

(d) $x_1 = 1.3 - \dfrac{(1.3^2 + e^{1.3} - 4)}{(2 \times 1.3 + e^{1.3})} = 1.08318$

$x_2 = 1.05831$

$x_3 = 1.05801$

$x_4 = 1.05801$

Therefore $x = 1.0580$ approximately

Vectors

1 $\sqrt{54}$ $\left(\text{or } 3\sqrt{6}\right)$

2 $\overrightarrow{BA} = \begin{pmatrix} 2 \\ 3 \\ 9 \end{pmatrix}$ $\overrightarrow{AC} = \begin{pmatrix} 4 \\ 6 \\ 18 \end{pmatrix}$

$\overrightarrow{AC} = 2\overrightarrow{BA}$ so $\overrightarrow{AC}$ and $\overrightarrow{BA}$ are parallel.

B, A and C are collinear (i.e. they lie on a straight line).

3 $\mathbf{r}_{AB} = 6\mathbf{i} + 2\mathbf{j} + \mathbf{k} + t(-\mathbf{i} + 2\mathbf{j} + 2\mathbf{k})$

Putting $t = -3$ gives C, so C lies on the line.

4 $6 - x = \dfrac{y - 2}{2} = \dfrac{z - 1}{2}$

5   $x = 2t + 3$ $y = t$ $z = 3t - 1$

   $\mathbf{r} = 3\mathbf{i} - \mathbf{k} + t(2\mathbf{i} + \mathbf{j} + 3\mathbf{k})$

6 (a) Lines meet at $3\mathbf{i} + 4\mathbf{j} + 6\mathbf{k}$

   (b) Angle between the lines is $80.4°$

7 $\overrightarrow{AB} = -9\mathbf{i} + 2\mathbf{j}$

  $\overrightarrow{AC} = -\mathbf{i} + 4\mathbf{j}$

  $\overrightarrow{BC} = 8\mathbf{i} + 2\mathbf{j}$

  $\overrightarrow{AC} \cdot \overrightarrow{BC} = -8 + 8 = 0$ *so*   AC is perpendicular to BC

  i.e. $\angle$ ACB is a right angle.

8 (a) Intersect

   (b) Perpendicular and intersect

   (c) Skew

Probability

1 (a) $P(A \cup B) = \dfrac{29}{84}$

   (b) A and B are not independent as $P(A \mid B) \neq P(A)$.

2 (a) $P(W) = \dfrac{3}{10}$

   (b) $P(V \mid W) = 0$

3 (a)

		Second die				
$\times$	1	2	3	4	5	6
1	1	2	3	4	5	6
2	2	4	6	8	10	12
First 3	3	6	9	12	15	18
die 4	4	8	12	16	20	24
5	5	10	15	20	25	30
6	6	12	18	24	30	36

   (b) $P(\text{even}) = \dfrac{27}{36} = \dfrac{3}{4}$

   (c) $P(\text{both } 3's \mid \text{odd product}) = \dfrac{\frac{1}{36}}{\frac{9}{36}} = \dfrac{1}{9}$

4 (a) $\dfrac{1}{36}$

   (b) $\dfrac{1}{8}$

   (c) $\dfrac{8}{27}$

5 (a)

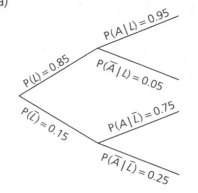

Hint: a tree diagram is a good approach.

Use L for leave on time.
A for arrive on time.

We need $P(L \cap A) = P(L)P(A \mid L)$
$$= 0.85 \times 0.95$$
$$= 0.8075$$

(b) We need $P(L \mid \overline{A}) = \dfrac{P(L \cap \overline{A})}{P(\overline{A})}$

From tree diagram.

Now $P(\overline{A}) = P(L \cap \overline{A}) + P(\overline{L} \cap \overline{A})$
$$= 0.85 \times 0.05 + 0.15 \times 0.25$$
$$= 0.08$$

So $P(L \mid \overline{A}) = \dfrac{0.85 \times 0.05}{0.08}$
$$= 0.53125$$

6 Let G be event 'Georgina goes first'
A be event 'Andrea goes first'
H be event 'First shot hits the target

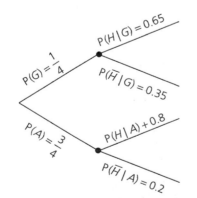

(a) $P(G \cap H) = P(G)\,P(H \mid G)$
$$= \frac{1}{4} \times 0.65 = 0.1625$$

(b) $P(\overline{H}) = P(G \cap \overline{H}) + P(A \cap \overline{H})$
$$= P(G)\,P(\overline{H} \mid G) + P(A)\,P(\overline{H} \mid A)$$
$$= \frac{1}{4} \times 0.35 + \frac{3}{4} \times 0.2$$
$$= 0.2375$$

(c) $P(H) = 1 - P(\overline{H}) = 0.7625$

$P(A \mid H) = \dfrac{P(A \cap H)}{P(H)}$

$$= \dfrac{P(A)\,P(H \mid A)}{P(H)}$$

$$= \dfrac{\dfrac{3}{4} \times 0.8}{0.7625} = 0.787 \ (3 \text{ s.f.})$$

Statistics

(a)

Sale price(£)	$0 \le x < 40000$	$40000 \le x < 50000$	$50000 \le x < 55000$	$55000 \le x < 60000$	$60000 \le x < 70000$	$70000 \le x < 85000$	$85000 \le x \le 110000$
Frequency density	0.0425	0.28	0.34	0.24	0.095	0.042	0.0448

(b)

Sale price	<40000	<50000	<55000	<60000	<70000	<85000	≤110000
Cumulative frequency	1700	4500	6200	7400	8350	8980	10100

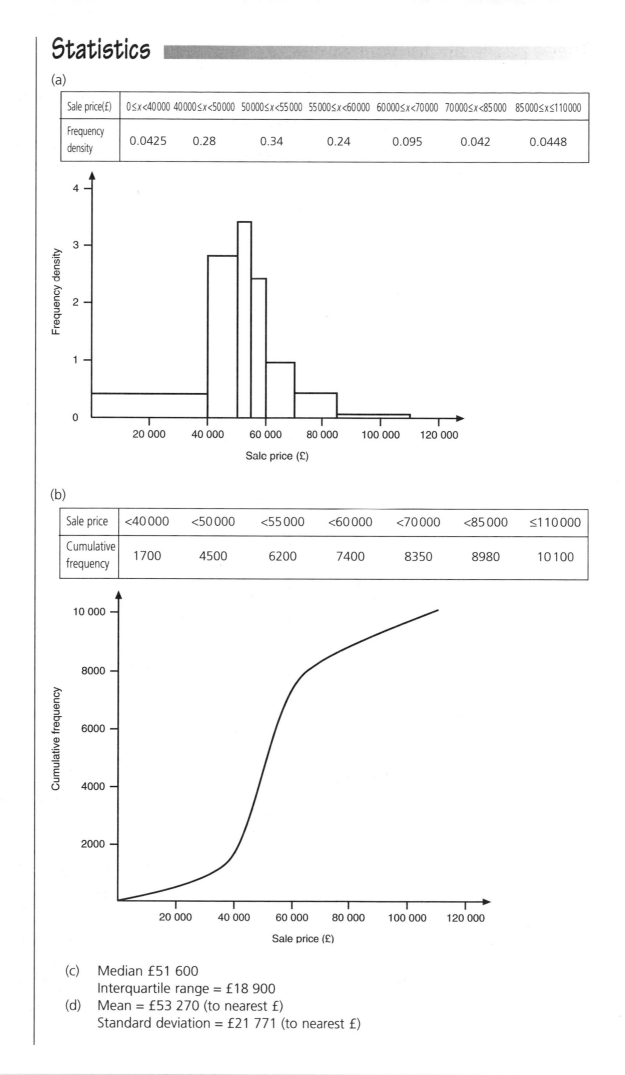

(c)   Median £51 600
      Interquartile range = £18 900

(d)   Mean = £53 270 (to nearest £)
      Standard deviation = £21 771 (to nearest £)

These pages are for your own notes.

Index

addition law 92
algebra techniques 7–9
algebraic juggling 11
angles 53–62, 90
    approximations 60
angles between lines 49
areas under curves 79–81
ascending powers 43
averages 98

binomial expansions 43–4
bracket expansion 7, 25

calculus basics 64
cartesian equations 89
chain rule 66–8
circular measures 61
common denominators 8
common difference 41–3
common ratio 42–3
complementary events 92
composite functions 20, 66
conditional probability 93
continuous functions
    roots 85–6
cosecant 57–8, 64, 73
cosine 45, 53–60, 64, 90
    integration 73, 75
cosine rule 55–6
cotangent 57, 64, 73
cubic inequalities 32
cumulative frequency curves
    97–8
curve sketching 50

data presentation 97
definite integrals 77–8
degrees 53
difference of two squares 9
differentiation 53, 64–7
discriminant 29
distance between points 47,
    49
domain 16

equations 7, 25, 48
    complex trigonometry
        58–9
    indices and logarithms
        37–8
    of a normal 71
errors 85
expressions 7

factor theorem 12, 32
factorisation 8, 28
first-order differential
    equations 78–9
formulae 7
    rearrangement 9
function type 16–17

geometric sequences 42–3

gradients 47–8, 64, 68, 71
graph sketching 50

histogram 97

identities 7, 58
    use of 76
independent events 93
indices
    functions 64, 73
    integration 76, 79, 82
    laws 34
    solving equations 37–8
inequalities 7
infinite series 43–4
integrals of functions 73
integration 53, 73–7
interquartile range 98–9
intersection of lines 89–90
inverse functions 20–1
    differentiation 66
    solutions 22
iterative solutions 86

linear equations 25
linear factors 13–14
linear inequalities 26
logarithms 35–8, 64
long division 11, 75

Maclaurin series 44–5
maximum point 30, 68–70
mean 98
median 98
mid-points of lines 49
minimum point 30, 68–70
mode 98
modulus 88
modulus function 17
mutually exclusive events 92

natural logarithms 35, 45,
    51, 64
    integration 73, 76, 79
Newton–Raphson procedure
    86
normal to a curve 71

parallel lines 48–9
partial fractions 13–14, 75
perpendicular lines 48–9
plotting two functions 51
point of inflexion 68–9
polynomials 10–12, 75
possibility space diagrams
    93–4
probability 92–5
product rule 65, 67, 70

quadratic equations 9,
    28–30, 32
    factors 13
    functions 28

graphs 30
    inequalities 31
quotient rule 65

radians 53
range of data 98–9
rates of change 68
rational functions 11
reflection 18–19
remainder theorem 12
reverse differentiation 74–5
right-angled triangles 53
roots 85–6

scalar product 90
scalar variable 88
secant 57–8, 64, 73
second derivative 68
sequence type 40–2
series
    ascending powers 43
    definition 40
    expansions 45
    infinite 43–4
sigma notation 41
simplification 25
simultaneous equations
    26–7, 32
sine 45, 53–60, 64
    integration 73, 75
sine rule 55–6
square roots 10
standard deviation 99
stationary points 68–70
straight line equations 48
stretch scale factor 18–19
surds 10

tangent 49, 53–5, 57–9, 62,
    64
    equation of 71
    integration 73, 75–6
three-dimensional angles
    61–2
three-dimensional
    coordinates 49
transformation of functions
    18–19
translation 18–19
tree diagrams 94–5
triangle area 60
trigonometric identities
    58–60
trigonometric units 53

variance 99
vector basics 88
vector equations 88–9
volumes of revolution 81–2